Science Web Reader

CHEMISTRY

First published in 2000 by:
Nelson Thornes (Publishers) Ltd
Delta Place
27 Bath Road
CHELTENHAM
GL53 7TH
United Kingdom

02 03 04 05 / 10 9 8 7 6 5 4 3 2

A catalogue record for this book is available from the British Library

ISBN 0 17 438738 5

Designed and typesetting by Mick Hodson Associates
Photo research by Zooid Pictures Limited

Printed and Bound in Croatia by Zrinski d. d. Cakovec

Author team:

Joan Solomon (Series Editor): Visiting professor at the Open University and King's College London. An experienced author who specialises in history of science and ethics and has written extensively at KS3/KS4.

Jan Murphy: Senior Lecturer in Science Education at John Moores University Liverpool.

Mary Ratcliffe: Senior Lecturer in Science Education at the University of Southampton. A-Level Chemistry author and Chair of examiners.

Nigel Heslop: Senior Science teacher, Oak Farm School. Consultant and author.

Richard Robinson: Television presenter and writer. Author of a series of books called *Science Magic*.

Every effort has been made to contact copyright holders. The publishers apologise to anyone whose rights have been overlooked and will be happy to rectify any errors or omissions at the earliest opportunity.

Acknowledgements
Cut-out illustration of 'Violet Beauregarde' by Quentin Blake from *Charlie and the Chocolate Factory* by Roald Dahl (Viking Children's Books, 1995). Copyright © Quentin Blake, 1995. Reprinted by permission of Penguin Books Ltd. Bettmann/Corbis UK Ltd. **1**; *Jan Hinsch*/Science Photo Library **6**; *Christine Osbourne*/Corbis UK Ltd. **8l**; *Giancarlo Negro*/Pyramids **8r**; *David Parker*/Science Photo Library **9**; *Giancarlo Negro*/Pyramids **10**; Biophoto Associates/Science Photo Library **11**; *Niall Benvie*/Corbis UK Ltd. **12**; *Deni Brown*/Oxford Scientific Films **13**; Archivo Iconografico, S.A./Corbis UK Ltd. **14**; NASA/*Roger Ressmeyer*/Corbis UK Ltd. **16l**; Science Science Photo Library **16r**; *Gilray*/Mary Evans Picture Library **26**; *Catherine Karnow*/Corbis UK Ltd. **28l**; Zooid Pictures **28r**; *Joe McDonald*/Corbis UK ltd. **30**; Hulton-Deutsch Collection/Corbis UK ltd. **35**; Imperial War Museum **36t**; B.A.S.F **36b**; *Sinclair Stammers*/Science Photo Library **38**; Mary Evans Picture Library **43**; Natural History Museum **44**; *Ron Watts*/Corbis UK Ltd. **45l**; Hulton-Duetsch Collections/Corbis UK Ltd. **45r**; Bettmann/Corbis UK ltd. **46**; Corbis UK Ltd. **47**; Bettmann/Corbis UK Ltd. **48**; Corbis UK Ltd. **50t**; Mercedes-Benz-Foto/Newspress Limited. **50b**; Ted Spiege/Corbis UK Ltd. **51**; Ford Motor Company (UK) **52**; *Charles D Winters*/Science Photo Library **56l**; *Robert Madden*/Oxford Scientific Films. **56**; *Andrew Syred*/Science Photo Library **59**; *JAL Cooke*/Oxford Scientific Films **60l**; *Paul Freeman*/Bridgeman Art Library **60r**; *Robert Opie* Collection **61t**; Topical Press/Hulton Getty Picture Collection Ltd. **61b**; Central Press/Hulton Getty Picture Collection Ltd. **62**

CONTENTS

Foreword

These readers for Science Web are a new departure for science education. They have been written for students of all sorts, for science enthusiasts who want to read more about modern science, for students who are on the humanities side and who like nothing more than curling up with a good story – whether about a scientist or anyone else, and for students who don't usually read much at all but enjoy cartoons and good illustrations. Some of the stories are about exciting new scientific discoveries, some are about scientific explorations in earlier times and a few describe applications of science or technology. They aim to keep school science up to date and interesting.

Teachers will find that the subject matter of each reading passage connects with science in the National Curriculum, even though the stories do not try to teach it in the usual way. Because the stories are related to real people we believe their science content will become more memorable. At the end of each article there is a selection of questions. These might be used by some teachers as part of the homework, or for classwork when students seem to need a quiet spell of self-learning. Other teachers may choose to adapt or even ignore the questions.

We believe that all the articles are suitable for some Key Stage 3 readers. We know that students in these years of schooling have a wide range of reading ages and rather than reduce the language to some lowest common denominator we decided to replicate the natural variety in two ways. Firstly we have provided stories with different styles, some deliberately exciting, some amusing, and some which pursue the search for a solution to some medical or similar problem. Our second way of providing variety is through the illustrations. Our artists have produced exceptionally fine pictures, some of which are quite beautiful. There are also photographs and cartoons.

These readers are designed to spread enthusiasm for science. It is changing so fast that we need to include up-to-the-minute discoveries. The stories from earlier times show that science has always been changing. It is, and was, the product of inventive men and women, so we have included human detail of how different scientists have reacted to challenges. Most importantly, these stories are designed to encourage students to get into the habit of reading about science, and so kindle a lifelong interest in it and in its progress.

Professor Joan Solomon
Series Editor
Science Web Readers

Cycles

You will have heard of the water cycle, the way water evaporates from the oceans, forms clouds in the atmosphere and falls as rain on the hills, running into rivers, then to the sea where it evaporates... and so on. There are some interesting variations on this recycling theme.

From dinosaurs to you

For instance, when you drink a glass of water, up to half of it is dinosaur pee! Unlikely? But think about it. There used to be lots of dinosaurs about. The planet was teeming with them for 150 million years, and they all had to have a drink or two, so what happened to the water after the dinosaurs had excreted what they didn't want? It drained through the ground into a river and joined the never ending cycle again, re-emerging millions of years later from a tap into your glass.

The water cycle: water molecules in dinosaur pee evaporate to form clouds and then fall as rain to become part of rivers.

Shells in your kettle!

What else is recycled along with the water? Have a look in a kettle. That coating of chalky fur on the heating element tells another story. While the dinosaurs ruled the Earth, the oceans were home to trillions of minute single-celled animals – plankton – each one protected from the waters around by a thin shell it constructed for itself from calcium, carbon and oxygen in the water. These calcium carbonate shells are still being made by plankton today, and they are beautiful structures, as elegant as pieces of fine jewellery, and only half a millimetre long.

When they died, those ancient creatures fell to the seabed – a continuous rain of tiny corpses that continued for billions of years. There, the flesh slowly disintegrated, but the chalky shells stayed around, building up thick layers of ooze, which settled and became, after a very long time, limestone rock. Some of this limestone got caught up in the water cycle, seeping into rainwater as it trickled through rocks towards a river, then to a reservoir, then towards your house. Tap water contains minute particles of these shells (they're what make 'hard water' hard). When the kettle is boiled, these tiny particles are forced out of the water and add to the crust, which slowly builds up on the heating element. Grandpa plankton's handiwork is once more building a shell-like structure, only not quite as elegant as his first effort billions of years ago.

Who's that you're eating?

What else gets recycled? You do! You are constantly losing skin cells. They get rubbed off, sometimes in sheets, as with dandruff, but more often in microscopic fragments so light that they float through the air and settle on the mantelpiece or some other surface – as dust! More than half of household dust is skin fragments. Odds are that some will end up on a lettuce leaf in your salad! That piece of 'you' that you've just eaten is then digested and your body finds that it has all the right ingredients to be turned into new you. Another cycle is completed.

Plankton cells found in a drop of seawater.

Carbon crisis

You will hear a lot about the carbon cycle in the news. Carbon dioxide (CO_2) has been fingered as the main cause of the Greenhouse Effect, the gradual warming of the Earth's atmosphere.

In its simplest form the carbon cycle goes like this: carbon is essential for all living things. Plants get it by breathing in the carbon dioxide that animals breathe out. Animals get it by eating the plants.

So far so good. The carbon goes round and round in a circle. The problem comes when the circle is disrupted. You see, carbon dioxide has another trick it can perform. It is a 'greenhouse gas', which means it lets through short wave radiation (blue light, ultraviolet rays) from space, but blocks long wave radiation (red and infra-red – ie heat) from being radiated back out. The more carbon dioxide there is, the more heat is kept in and the hotter the planet gets. This has far-reaching consequences.

The carbon cycle: the cow eats plants while it breathes out carbon dioxide that plants make into more plant stuff.

Earth story

When the Earth was formed 4.6 billion years ago it was a very, very hot place indeed, partly because there was a lot of carbon dioxide floating about in the atmosphere. As soon as plankton life appeared, a billion years later, carbon began to be used. Those simple life forms incorporated it into their shells and used it to build their bodies. Later on, as plants spread across the globe, they hoovered up all of the carbon dioxide. When the plants and animals died they formed layers of organic material – coal, peat, oil, gas – the 'fossil fuels'. Because the carbon was locked away inside the plant and plankton remains there was less carbon dioxide in the air, and the climate became cooler. By the time humans appeared on the scene two-and-a-half million years ago 95 per cent of the available carbon dioxide had been stowed away underground and the world was cool enough for our ancestors to survive.

But since mankind has begun to dig up and burn the fossil fuels, and to cut down the trees that 'fix' the carbon (turn it into carbohydrate), the temperature has begun to rise again in step with the increase in atmospheric carbon dioxide. Scientists predict that global temperatures could rise by 6°C over the next 50 years – 6°C is the difference between the hot and cold pools in your local leisure centre.

If we're irresponsible in our use of the Earth's fuel resources we could return the planet to its temperature of three billion years ago – that's one cycle we don't want to complete!

QUESTIONS

1. What are the two main cycles described in this article?
2. What is the chemical process called in which plants use carbon dioxide and turn it into carbohydrate?
3. The author describes the recycling of the material making up skin. In what way is this not like the other cycles? What sort of chemicals are needed to build new skin cells?
4. Name three fossil fuels mentioned in the article.
5. Name two things the author mentions as having increased the levels of carbon dioxide in the air.
6. Describe using words and pictures how limestone rocks can be formed.

Global warming: when we burn fossil fuels, like coal, we make lots of carbon dioxide, which stops the Earth losing heat.

Strange glass in the desert

There are billions of tons of sand on our Earth. Some of it is on beaches, some in deserts and some in inland places where it is quarried. We use sand for making cement and also for making glass. Window glass, for example, is made from sand mixed with limestone and soda, and heated up until it softens, at about 500°C. Then it is allowed to cool down slowly. But sand alone can also be made into a kind of glass called 'silica glass' if it is heated to a much higher temperature, well over 1000°C. Even the surface of the Moon is covered with very small silica glass 'marbles'.

Mystery in The Great Sand Sea

There is a part of the hot Sahara desert called 'The Great Sand Sea' where there are huge wind-swept mountains of sand. Nothing grows here, but legends are told about wealthy cities, one whole oasis, and complete ancient armies buried beneath the sand. None of those has been found, but explorers have recently come across pieces of amazing clear yellow-green glass that glitter like jewels in the sand.

They discovered places in the desert where small glassy chips were scattered about near larger chunks of glass. The explorers guessed that this was where prehistoric people had been chipping away at lumps of this rare and lovely glass. What were they making? No one is quite sure, but a good clue emerged in 1996. At an exhibition of objects found in the tomb of the famous boy-Pharaoh Tutankhamen there was one that caught the attention of two scientists. It was a fantastic many-coloured necklace. At its centre was a 'scarab' or beetle that had been carved out of green glass.

The scarab's light

The scientists eventually got permission from the Egyptian police to open the case and measure the colour of the light coming through the glass of the scarab. It was almost exactly the same range of colours as light from the desert glass that they had found 700 kilometres away. That told them more about the ancient Egyptians, but not much about the glass.

An area of the Sahara Desert where green glass was found.

The necklace from Tutankhamen's tomb.

Origin of the desert glass

The big mystery was how this silica glass in the desert had been formed. The scientists showed that it was purer than any known glass. They knew that when red hot magma from a volcano pours into the sea and cools down rapidly, it also makes silica glass. But that is only 75 per cent pure. The green desert glass was an astonishing 98 per cent pure! It has a melting point of 1700°C. More surprising still, it could be heated red-hot, poured into ice-cold water, and yet not shatter into pieces like other sorts of glass do. How was it made?

A German scientist was the first to come up with an idea. Thinking about how solids can be purified, he suggested that the glass had been made long ago in a hot volcanic lake. He had already found evidence of such a lake nearby. He guessed that, over thousands of years, some silica might have dissolved into the hot lake. Then, he thought, when this solution cooled down, pure silica glass might have formed at the bottom of the lake.

The idea seemed good, until a group of French scientists started investigating the remains of the old lake. They soon found that the dates did not fit. The glass was more than 28 million years old, but the age of the lake was only 9000 years.

Hot comets and meteorites

Then the French scientists started their own experiments. They observed the strange yellow-green glass very carefully under a powerful microscope and saw some tiny black marks. What were they? To find out, the scientists bombarded the spots with high-powered radiation and identified a rare element called iridium. This is mostly found in meteorites and comets. (The meteorite impact that may have been responsible for wiping out the dinosaurs left traces of iridium all over the Earth.) So, the French scientists who were investigating the green silica glass wondered if it could have been formed by a meteorite colliding with the Earth.

Their idea was that a hot comet or meteorite might have smashed into the ground with so much energy that some of the sand had not just melted – it had vaporised! Then, as the vapour cooled down, probably rather fast, it

A giant meteorite crater – could an impact like this create the coloured glass?

Fragment of meteorite glass, lying in the sand of the Libyan Desert.

would have condensed into a liquid, and then solidified into glass. It could not have solidified very slowly because crystals are made when that happens. You can tell from the pictures that the glass is smooth and rounded, with no sharp edges. On the other hand this evaporation and condensation is rather like the way we purify liquids in the laboratory, so the scientists guessed that it would make very pure glass.

But there were problems with this idea, too. In places where there definitely have been meteorite impacts the silica glass made is blackened, not clear. It has also melted into lumps that include bits of the local rock. Why didn't this happen in the 'The Great Sand Sea'?

Another problem was that no one could find any trace of a collision. Photographs taken by satellite showed nothing. Even radar cameras on NASA's special satellite, which can probe down beneath the sand, did not find the remains of a crater.

So the yellow-green silica glass in the desert is still a mystery. Could a passing comet have pulled up sand and heated it in the air? Could super-heated steam have made a spray of dissolved silica? What did make this beautiful stuff? Have you got any ideas?

QUESTIONS

1. List three differences between ordinary glass and silica glass.
2. Laboratory test tubes are sometimes made of silica glass even though it is more expensive than other types. Why?
3. What does the story about the scarab necklace tell us about the ancient Egyptians?
4. Explain the connection between the German scientist's idea about how the green silica glass was made, and how you might make pure salt from dirty salt in the laboratory.
5. What discovery by the French scientists was evidence for their theory about a meteorite collision? Explain this.
6. Explain why the French scientists' idea was rather like the distillation of water.
7. Explain your idea about how the strange yellow-green glass might have been made, and give your evidence for this idea.

A cure for scurvy

In the ancient world sailors never dared to go very far out from the shore. They had no maps and no way to find out where they were at sea. However, by the year 1100AD most European ships had a compass so that they knew which direction was north. But they still had a problem. They could not help being blown about by the wind and often finished up wrecked on rocks by the shore. Some 300 years later ship-builders had begun to learn how to move their sails round so that they could steer the ship on the right course, even when the wind was not directly behind them.

Fifteenth-century sailing ship.

The Curse of the Mouth

Portuguese sailors were the first to set off south to go around Africa, and across the Indian Ocean, on their way to the famous 'Spice Islands' of the East Indies. It took them months to reach Mombasa (in present-day Kenya). The sailors had all become terribly ill. First their gums became so black and swollen that they could not eat. Then old wounds opened up and bled. Sometimes their arms and legs swelled up and became so hard that they could not move. At this point Arab merchants arrived with baskets of large delicious oranges. The sailors ate them and all were completely cured within six days! The ship sailed on to the Spice Islands where they loaded up with cinnamon, nutmeg and ginger. On the way back there were bad storms. It took the Portuguese twelve weeks to cross the Arabian Sea back to Mombasa. Once more the sailors fell ill, with the disease they now called 'The Curse of the Mouth'. Some died, but once they reached land and got oranges to eat they recovered within just a few days.

About the same time Christopher Columbus set out on his famous voyage across the Atlantic Ocean to America (West Indies). This journey was not too long and the sailors did not get ill. Other ships were less lucky. Any ship which tried to cross the huge Pacific Ocean from Mexico to the Philippines always got the dreadful disease and sometimes the sailors died.

This illness was called 'scurvy', and it was not really new. Lots of people in Shakespeare's England got scurvy rather mildly at the end of almost every winter. The phrase 'You scurvy knave!' was an insult that Shakespeare often used.

Early cures

In those days there was no electricity, no fridges, and no freezers. Meat could only be kept from going bad by salting it. So most people just ate porridge, stewed salt pork, and soup with bread. There was no fruit like oranges or lemons, except for the very wealthy. The poorer people could not afford meat, some had apples stored through the winter and some put vegetables such as turnips and herbs in their stews.

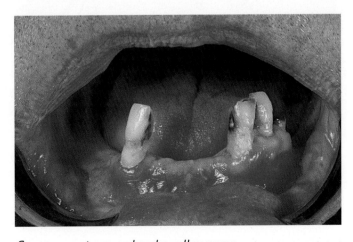

Scurvy symptoms: red and swollen gums.

What the doctors could not understand was why the poor got less scurvy than the rich people! They tried lots of different cures that were cheaper than oranges – vinegar, sulphuric acid, scurvy grass, sorrell leaves, and water cress. Some of them seemed to work when people had only mild scurvy.

Most of these remedies contained acids. Even sorrel leaves, which are very common, taste as sharp as lemon juice or a sour apple. You can nibble the leaves (if they have been identified and washed), or do a test for acids by crushing any of these onto blue litmus paper.

In 1740 Britain sent out seven warships to seize the silver treasure from the Spanish galleons in South America. Three years later only one British ship returned to England, with just 145 sailors on board. All the rest had died horrible deaths from scurvy. British sailors were usually given a gallon of beer to drink each day, and a pound of hard 'ship's biscuit'. There was also some salted meat, some beans and vinegar – but still no expensive oranges and lemons.

Scurvy grass: eating it protected sailors against the disease.

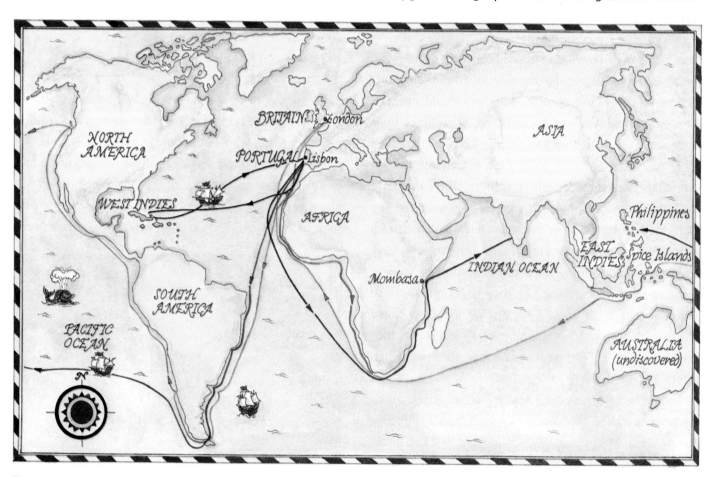

The ocean trade routes of the sixteenth and seventeenth centuries.

Common sorrell.

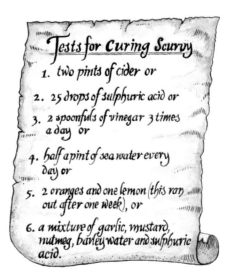

Some old tests for curing scurvy.

Oranges, lemons... and 'limeys'

Then, in 1747, a Scottish naval doctor decided to do some really scientific tests to find out what substances cured scurvy. Dr James Lind waited until the sailors on his ship fell ill with scurvy. Then he carefully selected six pairs of them who all seemed equally ill. He gave each pair different 'cures':

The result after six weeks was that only the oranges and lemons cured both the sailors' scurvy. The cider just helped a bit.

Few people took any notice of these results. They said to James Lind, 'Where is your hypothesis?', 'What is your explanation?' Most people still thought that it might be due to bad air in foreign countries.

When people tried making concentrated lemon juice by boiling it up to evaporate the water, it tasted even more acid but no longer seemed to cure scurvy. The Navy decided to use fresh lime-juice on the long journeys to Australia and New Zealand, which usually worked. (Australians still call British people 'limeys'.)

It was not until well into the twentieth century that scientists could show that the acid needed was not sulphuric, nor vinegar, nor even lemon juice (citric acid) but vitamin C, which is ascorbic acid. This is in all sorts of fresh food but is destroyed by heat. We can even make it in the laboratory.

QUESTIONS

1. Give two reasons why in early times boats could not sail off to the Spice Islands.
2. Why does the article ask you to use blue and not red litmus paper for the test on sorrel leaves?
3. Do you think that Dr Lind's tests were really fair?
4. Why did Dr Lind have two sailors, both equally ill, for each of his tests?
5. Do you think Dr Lind should have given oranges to all the ill sailors?
6. Make a list of all the fruits you know that taste acidic.
7. Sailors often got scurvy when they reached Mombasa. Some of the sailors thought that this was because they had been too long without fresh acidic fruit. Others thought this proved that scurvy was in the bad smelling air around Mombasa.
   List the evidence for the two theories. Then explain which one of the two explanations for getting scurvy was right.

Elements and medicines

There are so many different substances in the world, some hard, some soft, some coloured and some transparent. When people first mixed and heated them they discovered that they changed. Sometimes the mixture became a molten metal, sometimes a smoking solid. The early chemists who carried out these experiments often asked themselves these two questions:

'Is this substance completely new, or is it made up from smaller bits (elements) of the substances we started with?'

'Would it be possible to get rich by heating up the right mixture of these elements to make gold?'

The Greek elements

The Greeks thought that the simple elements were probably Earth, Air, Fire and Water. It was not a very good guess, although the Earth does contain a great variety of beautiful crystals and rocks with useful metal ores. The Egyptians did better. They found that heating things with fire, or dissolving them in water, often seemed to change them completely (think of salt). So they thought about what looked and felt hot, cold, dry or wet. They discovered that heating metals with sulphur or wood could often change their colour until they looked like something else. They learnt how to dye lots of things – glass, fabric and even metals. But if their dyed silver looked like gold, was it really gold? You can see their problem.

Islam and the search for the Elixir of Life

The year 622AD was very important. This was when the Prophet Mohammed began teaching about Islam, one of the world's great religions. His followers carried his ideas to other countries, conquering almost half the world and converting people to Islam and teaching them Arabic. This was also important for science, because the Arabs became very interested in mathematics, medicine and chemistry. As they travelled across their huge empire from Portugal and Spain in the west to the far away borders of China in the east, they could talk to many different people and learn from their ideas. This included the chemical ideas of the Egyptians.

The Arabs wanted to make a more important substance than gold – a medicine that would cure all illnesses and help them to live for ever. They called it the 'Elixir of Life'. Doctors often felt the foreheads of their patients as they do today. They thought that a healthy body shouldn't feel too hot or too dry, too wet or too cold; the four elements had to be in perfect balance for the person to be healthy.

Arabian scientists.

The first Arabian scientists

For centuries the Arabian scientists, like Jebir, Al-Razi and Avicenna, travelled between the great cities of the east and west. They rode across vast deserts and along the old silk trails that led from Europe into Asia. After they had tied up their horses or camels for the night, they talked together during the cold starlit evenings, about the mysteries of different substances. The Arabs were great story-tellers. Jebir worked at the court of Caliph (Emperor) Haroun Al Rashid, who was famous for the thousand and one stories of the Arabian Nights. He told about how the Egyptians had mixed sulphur and mercury, and heated them for forty days and forty nights until they changed to a gold colour. The doctors drew diagrams in the sand showing how the human organs – heart, brain, spleen and liver – were like air, water, earth and fire within the body, and how the Elixir might bring them all into perfect balance.

These Arab scientists made the first alkalis and found they were the 'opposite' to acids in many ways, and yet could burn the skin as badly as any acid. They made alcohol, although they did not drink it, found that it was cold on the skin, and yet lit easily with a blue flame. The balance of chemicals was not easy to understand.

The Arabs believed that God had made the whole world to be in perfect balance. The moon and planets circled round in the sky in regular cycles of time. The mathematicians invented magic number squares that were also in 'balance', but in a different way (see below).

2	9	4
7	5	3
6	1	8

Magic number square.

Great discoveries

Avicenna's most important ideas were about how doctors could cure people by improving the balance within a human body. Some medicines would produce more heat, and some needed to be either acidic or alkaline. By the time he died, (30 years before William the Conqueror landed in England), he had written more than 100 books, which were used to teach doctors in all the medical schools of Europe. In India, and many Arab countries his ideas are still taught today. Neither Avicenna nor any other scientist ever managed to find the Elixir of Life, but they had some great successes:

- They made and named most of the common chemicals that we use in the school laboratory today. They also discovered petroleum, which they used in a special burner, like the Bunsen burner, for their experiments.
- They linked mathematics, chemistry and medicine so that future scientists would know the importance of taking measurements, to distil and purify chemicals, and to use small quantities for making new medicines.

QUESTIONS

1. Name two chemical compounds that look quite different, but both contain copper.
2. Think of two substances that look the same but are really different. Draw up a table in two columns showing the ways in which they are similar and the ways in which they are, or could be, different.
3. The temperature of the human body and its rate of breathing should normally be the same – in balance – as Avicenna taught.
   What should each of them be if the person is healthy? When you are ill and your temperature goes up, what happens to your rate of breathing?
4. Do you think that scientists will ever be able to make the Elixir of Life? Why?

What killed the Red Planet?

If you look at the planet Mars from Earth it only seems just a little more red than the other planets and stars. But from a spaceship going round it, or even on its surface looking through half-closed eyes, Mars might well be a living and watery world. You can make out what seem to be winding river beds that have worn some of the rocks. There are also flat lands that might have been flooded during rainy seasons thousands or millions of years ago.

No water – no life

There is still some carbon dioxide in the atmosphere of Mars, and there is oxygen combined with iron in its red rocks. Almost a perfect place, you would have thought, to find simple living creatures like some of those we know on Earth. Yet the planet is quite dry. It is further out from the Sun than the Earth and terribly cold on its surface during the night, colder than −100°C. The winter, which is far colder still, lasts for almost two of our years. We have known for a long time that there are ice-caps at the Martian north and south poles, but this is not water ice, just a thin layer of frozen carbon dioxide. Without water there can be no life.

In 1976 an unmanned spaceship from NASA, called 'Viking', landed on the Martian surface. The remote-control experiments were unpacked by robots and these analysed the Martian atmosphere and soil, and even dug under a rock or two. It was searching for drops of precious water, some long dead organic material, or a single bacterium. None were found.

Suspended animation

Some scientists had a theory that, long ago, life on Mars might have been frozen or dried out into a form where it

Mars showing the winding riverbeds.

Mars probe Viking.

could still exist in suspended animation. Then it would be ready to come to life again if, or when, it got water or plant nutrients. The scientists predicted that, as the ancient organism came to life and started respiring, there would be a release of carbon dioxide from it. The experiment was carried out by the 'Viking' spaceship. You can imagine the excitement when the robot arms tested the atmosphere around where the nutrients had been added and did find traces of extra carbon dioxide being produced. Brilliant! Was an ancient Martian organism waking up? Unfortunately, further digging found no organic material in the soil that could have been part of a plant, animal or even a bacterium. A possible explanation was that the carbon compounds in the nutrients themselves had simply been oxidised by the red oxygen-rich Martian sand and rocks, and turned into carbon dioxide gas.

That was a disappointment. Since then, four spaceships, two from Russia and two from the United States, have set out for Mars, but each one of them either crashed or just went silent. However, another spaceship has recently been successfully launched towards the Red Planet. It will, we hope, land at the edge of the southern polar ice-cap and search the atmosphere and the rocks for evidence to help us understand the history of Mars.

Almost all the scientists agree that Mars was once a much warmer, wetter place where life could have flourished long ago, at the time our own Earth was still a hot and hostile place full of erupting volcanoes. We have recovered pieces of old meteorites that fell to Earth millions of years ago which seem to be made of Martian rock. One even had traces of something that might have been a fossilised bacterium from Mars! It was very small and faint, so no one is quite sure.

What killed Martian life?

There are three theories about what killed life on Mars:

THEORY 1. Large meteorites or an asteroid might have crashed into Mars and just blown away its atmosphere, together with any water vapour. The orbits of the asteroids are much nearer Mars than Earth.

THEORY 2. Carbon dioxide gas makes a 'greenhouse effect' and could have kept the planet much warmer. But carbon dioxide dissolves in rock and water to make carbonates. It also does this on the Earth, but we have plants, which use the carbon dioxide for photosynthesis. They only store the carbon for a short time, releasing it slowly as the plant material decomposes. Without green plants on Mars all the carbon dioxide might have been trapped in the soil and rocks. No greenhouse effect, no heat and no water.

THEORY 3. Maybe Mars is just going through a very severe Ice Age because the Sun is cooler. There seems to be some evidence of different layers in the rocks. Could there have been many Ice Ages? Will Mars become warm and living once again when the Ice Age passes?

QUESTIONS

Imagine that the Mars 'Surveyor' spaceship has performed its experiments. It has produced results and it is your job to decide which of the three theories is most likely to be right in each case.

a) Digging down, 'Surveyor' found layers of rock that were less red. By adding acid to these rocks it has found that the deeper ones produced less carbon dioxide than the rocks nearer the surface.

b) Evidence from the Martian rocks shows that there have been several long periods when there was plenty of water and oxygen, and other times when there was no water and only some carbon dioxide.

c) Evidence from the rocks shows that the climate of Mars changed quite suddenly from being warm and wet, to dry and cold, exactly two billion years ago.

Explain your answers carefully, and decide what other experiments, if any, you would like to carry out to collect more evidence for life on Mars.

Priestley's air

All invisible gases look the same as air – but they can have very different effects. Down in coal mines there is sometimes an invisible gas that can smother and even kill people. That is why miners never go underground alone. If one could not breathe, and collapsed, others could hold their breath and pull him back into the 'fresh air'.

Different 'airs'

Then, about 200 years ago, a man called Joseph Priestley wrote a book about these different 'airs', or gases as we call them now. He even discovered one gas that could be used as an indicator for the quality of air in mines. If the air was fresh and good to breathe his indicator gas, which was as transparent as air, turned dark brown. If it was used with any other gas the indicator gas stayed transparent. That was life-saving for miners.

At one time, Joseph Priestley lived next door to a brewery. As the beer fermented he saw a great cloud of the

An invisible gas often caused miners to collapse – even die.

gas he called 'fixed air' hanging over it. The workers told Priestley that they had to escape and have a good breath of fresh air from time to time. Priestley became so interested in this 'fixed air' that he tried making it in his laboratory at home. He poured some acid on natural chalk and found that it bubbled up making lots of this 'fixed air', which we now call carbon dioxide. When he bubbled this gas into water he found he had made a delicious sparkling drink. Soft drinks all use the same method today!

Priestley's candle experiments

Priestley's next experiments explored the burning of candles. When he burnt a candle inside a closed jar the flame always went out after a minute or two. He wondered if this might have something to do with the smoke that came off the candle, or if it was yet another example of 'fixed air'.

Joseph Priestley investigating his 'fixed air'.

Joseph Priestley was very interested in the gas left inside the jar. Was it 'fixed air'? He put a lighted candle into it. The flame went out at once! Would it smother an animal as it had smothered the miners?

Priestley caught a little house mouse and put it in the jar. Soon it had trouble breathing, and fell over. Some of the mice that Priestley experimented with died. But he found that if he picked the mouse out of the jar quickly and rubbed it carefully, it would soon start breathing again. It was just like the miners whose friends had pulled them out into the fresh air.

Unexpected results

Priestley also tried his 'fixed air' on a green plant. He put it inside the jar of air that would put out a flame, or kill a mouse. He screwed down the lid firmly and put the jar in the sunlight on the window-sill. Priestley expected the plant to die, but two weeks later it still looked fine. Then he found out the most extraordinary thing! The gas inside the

jar did NOT put out a flame or kill a mouse any more. It was like fresh air again!

Priestley wrote all this down in his great book on 'Different Kinds of Air'. Then he added:

'There is an old saying that if green moss is growing inside a well, the water will stay fresh – now I know why this is true! Everyone should plant trees by their houses to keep the air good to breathe.'

Priestley added acid to chalk to make 'fixed air'.

TRY YOUR OWN EXPERIMENT!

Diagram 1

1. Get two screw top jars, one large and one small.
2. For each one, fix a small birthday cake candle to the lid with plasticine (Diagram 1).

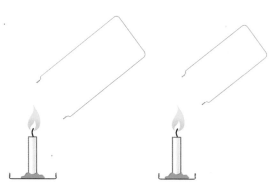

Diagram 2

3. Light the candle and quickly screw down the jar over it. (Diagram 2)
   Watch what happens.
4. Discuss your observations with a friend, and make up an explanation for them.
   Write down the experimental evidence first, and then your theory.

TRY ANOTHER EXPERIMENT LIKE PRIESTLEY'S!

1.

2.

3.

4.

1. Light a small birthday cake candle on a lid as before and place a jar over it.
2. Wait for the smoke in the jar to clear.
3. Then turn the jar the right way up and light another candle.
4. Put the candle into the jar. What happens?

QUESTIONS

1. How many different gases do you know? Write down their names.
2. What 'indicator' have you used in the school laboratory? What makes it go different colours?
3. Do you think it was cruel of Priestley to use mice in his experiments? Was it important? Write down the reasons for your answer and discuss them with your group.
4. Priestley did not know about the 'oxygen theory of burning', or respiration or about photosynthesis. That was all discovered later. If you have learnt about any of those theories, try Question **5**.
5. Write a letter to 'The Reverend Joseph Priestley'. Explain to him our modern ideas about burning, and why the little mice died while the green plant did not.

Cars, cars and more cars

Two couples Peter, Carol, Jane and Ian are talking about how they travel around...

Cars are exhausting!

Most modern cars in this country run on unleaded petrol or diesel. Their exhaust fumes contain carbon dioxide, water vapour and nitrogen dioxide. Burning fossil fuels, such as petrol, adds more carbon dioxide to the atmosphere and scientists think that an increase in carbon dioxide is causing global warming. Worse, nitrogen dioxide is acidic and is involved in making 'acid rain'. If the number of cars on the road increases, air pollution will increase. So, many people want to reduce pollution and use renewable fuels.

Peter and Carol say...

We don't own a car. We travel everywhere by public transport or bike. It's much better for the environment. Owning a car is expensive - you have to pay a lot to look after it and then there's the fuel and road tax. You're paying even when you're not using it. We bike to work and get there quicker than people who get stuck in traffic jams. It keeps us really healthy.

We use trains and buses to go out in the evenings. We visit a lot of people and have a good social life. If we're going anywhere really late, we get a taxi - we don't have to watch what we drink and it's still cheaper in the long run. We think car owners should pay more in taxes - think of all the damage they're doing to the environment.

Jane and Ian say...

We've just bought a new car. It's really comfortable and reliable. We use it every day - to go to work, shopping, the gym, everything really. Even if it's sometimes difficult to find a parking space. We need a car - we couldn't possibly rely on public transport for all we do. We know that cars can add to pollution, but modern cars are well designed. A lot of work has gone into reducing emissions.

We like modern cars - they're safe and easy to drive. We buy a new car every few years, so that we're taking advantage of all the new features. We don't like using trains and buses - they're unreliable and often crowded and dirty. When we're earning more money, we'll each have a car, so we can always do what we want.

WHAT IT TAKES TO BUILD A CAR

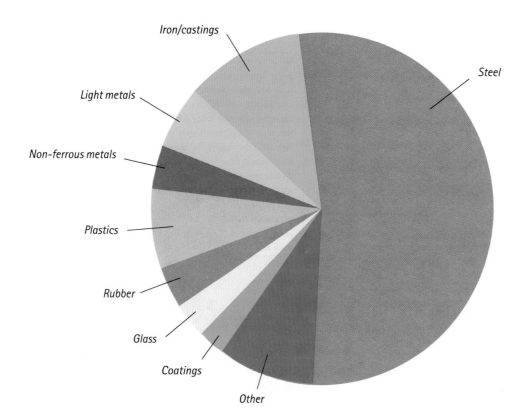

Iron/castings

Light metals

Non-ferrous metals

Plastics

Rubber

Glass

Coatings

Other

Steel

Source:
'What it takes to build a car',
from *The Motor Car –
Understanding Global Issues*
published by European Schoolbooks
Publishing Limited.

A technological solution

Technology may come to our aid. In Iceland, they are hoping to use hydrogen as the main fuel for transport in the future. There is a lot of water in Iceland and water can be broken down chemically to give hydrogen. This process requires electricity and is only sensible where electricity is made from a renewable energy source – like hydro-electricity or geothermal energy.

Fuel cells use oxygen from the air and hydrogen to power cars electrically. Water is the only exhaust gas, but as hydrogen is a very inflammable gas, it has to be stored carefully. Technologists are solving the storage and design problems. DaimlerChrysler, the car manufacturer, has developed a car that will run on hydrogen. They are likely to mass-produce this car in the near future and Iceland may become the first country to rely on hydrogen, a renewable fuel, rather than on fossil fuels.

Even if there are improvements in car design, it doesn't mean the environment will automatically benefit. It still costs a lot in raw materials to make cars.

Choices have consequences

Car use is currently on the increase worldwide. Many factors affect the transport we use – costs, convenience, government policy, fuel availability, personal lifestyle and so on. There are ethical issues in car use. How can we get the best for everybody – ourselves, car manufacturers and their employees, future generations, wildlife and the natural environment? One way to help consider different sides of a problem is to use a 'consequence map', which looks at 'What if?' questions. This may help us see the advantages and disadvantages of different actions. It doesn't answer problems. But it can show where we're looking at scientific evidence and where we're using our own opinions or values.

Let's consider the question: 'What if certain cars could only be used on certain days, for example cars with registration letters G-M can only be used on Mondays, Wednesdays and Fridays?' The consequence map on page 23 helps to answer this question.

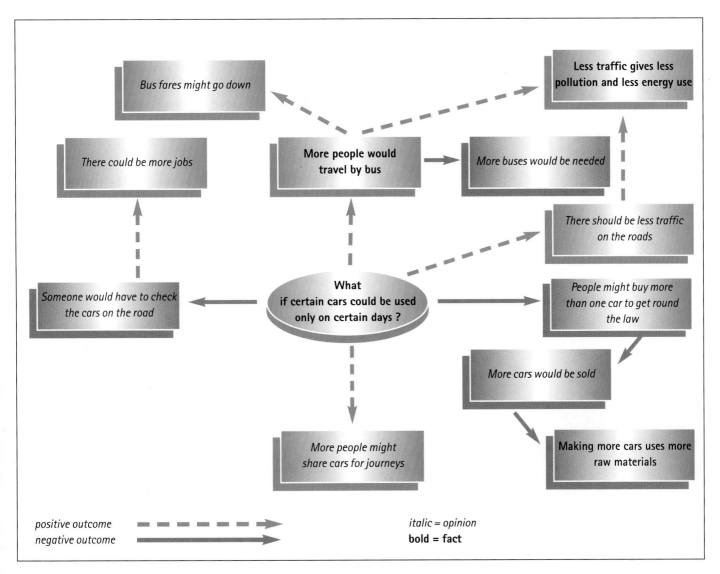

positive outcome ┅┅┅→
negative outcome ────→

italic = opinion
bold = fact

Consequence map.

QUESTIONS

1. Why is it not sensible to make hydrogen using electricity from oil- or gas-fired power stations?

2. Peter, Carol, Jane and Ian have their own views. List the points they make that are facts and those that are opinions.

3. Try drawing consequence maps for any of these 'What If?' questions. Show where you're using facts and where you're using opinions.
   What if... ?
   ... a person could buy only one new car every 10 years?

... the tax on car fuel was increased by ten times?

... the amount of petrol you could buy depended on the job you did?

... motorways were closed to cars that only contained one person?

... all new cars had to be made from 75 per cent recycled materials?

... you had to show that you travelled 10 miles by public transport for every 10 miles you travelled by car?

Think of your own 'What if?' questions.

The Californian gold rush

Nowadays, when we think of California, we think of Hollywood and film stars. But it was gold that first made California famous throughout the world. Here is the story of a 'forty-niner' – a man who went there in 1849 to make his fortune.

'So what I did was dig up a spadeful of mixed soil and stones from the river and tip it into my pan. Then I added water and swirled it all round and round, and then tipped out the water and stones on top. Then I added more water and went on swirling and throwing out. Finally, when the soil and stones had all gone, I could sometimes see the small pieces of gold gleaming at the bottom of the pan. That was a great moment! Oh no, it never got rusted over. Gold never rusts, it always gleams like new. I still dream about those gleaming bits of gold every night.'

'Hi, youngster! My name is Johann. My family came to America from Germany as immigrants last century. We were very poor, so when I heard about the gold in southern California I joined in the great 'Gold Rush' right across the plains of America, escaping from the Indians, and finally arriving at Sacramento. It was just a small village then on a fast flowing river. At the store I bought myself some provisions – flour, whisky, ammunition for my gun, a blanket, and a shallow dish for 'panning' out the gold. At first I was very excited, and sure I would become rich.'

'The gold dust comes down the river. No, you can't see it on top of the stones. Gold is heavy and sinks down to the bottom. We call it gold 'dust' because the pieces of it are so small, but it is not like the dust you could sweep up from the kitchen floor. It's very heavy – heavier than lead if you compare pieces of the same size.'

'It was a hard life. I shot bear or chipmunk or anything else I could get to cook for supper. I slept in a rough shack I made for myself, and didn't wash for a year or more! And no, bless you, I never got rich, neither. One very bad year I found a place where there were more gleaming golden pieces, but they didn't seem quite right. I spent months and months in the rain and wind panning and panning until my arms ached. It never seemed to settle down to the bottom properly. But it did gleam like gold!'

'Then an old miner came along. He watched me and he just laughed and laughed. He took a little of this gold and put it in the fire. It didn't melt, but it smelt dreadful! It was like burning sulphur, and at the end there was nothing left but iron rust.'

'"There you are," said the old miner, "No one but a fool would call that gold! It's only Fools' Gold. You wouldn't have got a penny for that!"'

'I reckon I was a fool in more than one way. The last time I came back to sell my gold dust at the store in Sacramento, the whole town had been rebuilt. Very few of the miners got rich, but store-keepers and the others did!'

'More than two billion dollars worth of gold has been found – California has got richer and richer, and Sacramento has become the state capital city. Just look at it now!'

'Goodbye, youngster, wish me luck! I've got my pan with me, my pack is full, and I'm off to look for silver and copper in the Rocky Mountains. Like to come with me?'

QUESTIONS

1. Gold and iron are both metals. Write down two differences between them.
2. Read the words about 'Fools' Gold' again.
   a) Why do you think that pieces of it would not settle to the bottom of the pan as quickly as real gold?
   b) If 'Fools' Gold' is not real gold, use information in the article to suggest what elements you think it is made from, and give reasons for your guess.
3. Find out all you can about mining for silver and copper. Then write a letter to the old miner, Johann, advising him how to recognise these metal ores and how to check that they really do contain silver and copper.

Discovery of an element

How many chemical elements are there? The modern Periodic Table shows symbols for 112. Some, like gold and copper, have been known for thousands of years. New synthetic elements are still being 'discovered'. Let's look at the discovery of one element to see how creative and imaginative scientists can be. New technology also plays a part in scientists' work.

Davy the discoverer

Humphry Davy was a most inventive chemist. He did a great number of important experiments during his life. For example, he experimented with laughing gas, often inhaling it himself. He also produced a safety lamp, helping to prevent explosions in coal mines. But he is probably best remembered for his discovery of several elements.

Davy was born in 1778 and started his chemical experiments in Bristol. He moved to the Royal Institution in London at the age of 22, where he gave lectures on chemistry and continued to experiment. His lectures were extremely popular at a time when chemistry was also very popular. A book written by Mrs Jane Marcet, entitled *Conversations on Chemistry* was a bestseller. Davy's work even inspired William Wordsworth to include references to chemistry in his poetry!

Electrifying experiments

In 1807 electrical cells were new technology. Davy experimented to see the effects of electricity on common materials. He saw that an electrical current could break down – decompose – chemical compounds, so he tried to decompose potash (potassium hydroxide). He found that electricity had no effect on solid potash, but he became very excited when he saw what happened when the potash had been melted by the electrical current. Globules of a shiny solid collected around the negative electrode.

We can get a glimpse of Davy's excitement in the report he wrote later for the Royal Society:

'... a vivid and constant light appeared... globules which inflamed in the atmosphere rose through the potash... There was a violent effervescence at the upper surface. At the lower, or negative, surface small globules

Gilray cartoon of Humphry Davy at the Royal Institution.

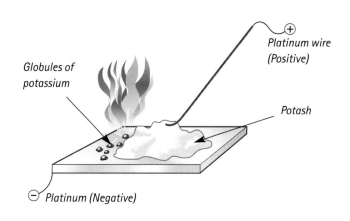

Davy made potassium by passing a current through potash.

having a highly metallic lustre, and being precisely similar in visible characters to quicksilver (mercury), appeared, some of which burnt with explosion and bright flame as soon as they were formed... The globules often burnt at the moment of their formation, and sometimes violently exploded and separated into smaller globules, which flew with great velocity through the air in a state of vivid combustion, producing a beautiful effect of continued jets of fire.'

New metals

Davy had to decide what these globules were. He had found a substance that was unknown until then. To begin with he called it *potagen* meaning 'generated from' potash. He then studied the properties of *potagen*. As we can see from his description, it was very reactive. It was also shiny like quicksilver – an old name for mercury. From the evidence he collected and his knowledge of chemistry, Davy decided it was a metal and said it should be called 'potassium'. In naming it potassium Davy was following a convention to name new metallic elements so that they ended in *-ium*. To begin with, not everyone agreed that it was a metal. Some chemists were uncertain about classifying it as a metal because it was much lighter than metals like copper and iron. As more was found out about this new element, most chemists agreed that it had properties of a metal and so potassium became the accepted name.

Davy added potassium to water and saw how violent the reaction was. Like most scientists, he tried to link different observations to construct a new idea. He thought this reaction was similar to the violence of a volcanic eruption so he suggested that eruptions might be caused by water coming into contact with deposits of potassium under the Earth's crust. We now know, of course, that this idea is wrong.

Spreading the word

Scientists share their work so that other scientists can build on evidence and ideas. Scientific research is reported in special journals or books. Davy published all his discoveries in this way. This is how he wrote about discovering potassium:

'To form potassium, potash in a thin piece is placed between 2 discs of platinum connected with the extremities of a voltaic apparatus of 200 double plates; it will soon undergo fusion, oxygene will separate at the positive surface and small metallic globules will appear at the negative surface, which consist of potassium. I discovered this metal in the beginning of October 1807.'

You can see that this description, written some time later, is rather different to Davy's report to the Royal Society.

Once Davy had realised he could isolate potassium from potash using electricity, he tried using electricity to break down other compounds. As a result he was the first person to find other metallic elements – sodium, magnesium, calcium, strontium and barium.

QUESTIONS

1. What evidence is needed to disprove (or prove) Davy's ideas about volcanic eruptions being reactions between potassium and water?
2. Why do you think Davy's journal account of the discovery of potassium written sometime after the event is different to his report to the Royal Society?
3. Write an account of an experiment you have done recently as:
   a) a newspaper article
   b) a report for other pupils, so that they can carry out the experiment.
4. Use a reference book, CD-ROM or web search to find out more about the properties of the metallic elements Davy discovered.
5. The Royal Institution was founded in London in 1799 to demonstrate the applications of science to the public. Find out more about the work of Davy, Faraday and the Royal Institution. The Royal Institution website is at **http://www.ri.ac.uk**

Body piercing

If you wear earrings, you don't want them to irritate your skin. The best quality earrings are made from metals like gold or silver, which don't react. These earrings can be expensive – so lots of earrings are sold that just have a coating of gold. The gold plating means the surface won't react with the skin, but the inside can be made of cheaper metal.

Irritating problem

Some cheap earrings can cause a lot of irritation. This may be because they contain too much nickel. Nickel is a hard, silvery metal. It can be combined with other metals to form alloys – a lot of coins are alloys of nickel and copper. Researchers have found that more people are becoming allergic to nickel on their skin. People with a nickel allergy can't wear jewellery with any nickel in contact with their skin.

The European Union (EU) gives a guide to how much nickel is allowed in jewellery. Earrings should contain less than 0.05 per cent nickel. This means that an earring weighing 6 g should have less than 0.003 g of nickel – a very tiny amount. What's more, only a trace amount of that nickel should be released onto the skin – less than 0.5 micrograms per square centimetre of surface per week! (There are 1 million micrograms in a gram.)

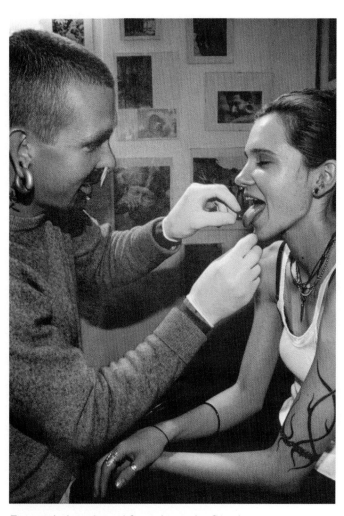

Tongue being pierced for a ring to be fitted.

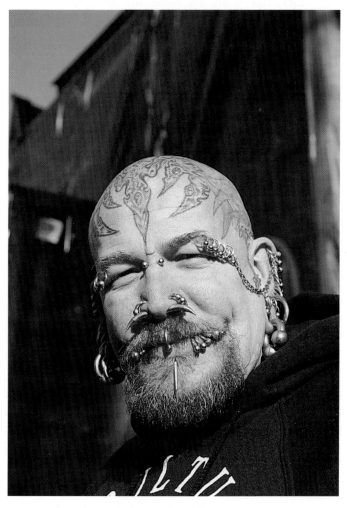

Here's a lot of metal! How safe is it?

Method 1	Method 2	Method 3
This is the one most government laboratories use. Swab each earring with a solution of a particular chemical (called dimethylglyoxime). This chemical should produce a red colour if any nickel is present.	Put each earring in contact with artificial sweat for a week. Rub the earring with the test chemical, as in Method 1.	Analyse the metal content of each earring using an atomic absorption spectrometer. This instrument is able to show precisely the quantities of all metals present in the whole earring.

Testing the makers' claims

Researchers in Finland decided to test earrings for their nickel content. They tested 66 different earrings imported from other European countries. All the makers claimed the nickel content was well below the EU limit.

The Finnish scientists had to use very sensitive tests to see if there was any nickel present. They tried three different methods (see Table above).

Antti Ponka and Asta Ekman from the Helsinki Centre for the Environment carried out the tests. Ponka says that the commonly used swab test, Method 1, gives misleading results. 'It's useless,' he says.

It's not easy for jewellers to meet the EU requirements. Stephen Carter, who works for a laboratory in South London, says: 'There's such a wide range of jewellery – it's quite difficult for importers to meet requirements. The best way to solve it is for people not to use nickel.'

Adapted from New Scientist, *30 Jan 1999, p22, 'Cheap and Nasty.'*

RESULTS Method	1	2	3
Number of earrings giving red colour	0	9	–
Number of earrings showing giving more nickel than the EU limit	0	9	25

Methods for testing earings for nickel.

QUESTIONS
1. Why do you think people make earrings that contain nickel?
2. Why do you think different methods of testing for nickel give different results?
3. Which method of testing the earrings do you think gives the most reliable result?
4. How sure do you think the researchers can be that many earrings cause nickel allergies?
5. Think about an experiment you have carried out recently. What sort of things affected how certain you could be that your results were accurate?
6. If you were looking for a new material to make ear-studs from, what properties would it need?
7. Why do you think ear-studs are not made from plastic?
8. Who should decide whether earrings contain nickel? The government? Scientists? People who wear earrings? People who make earrings? Explain your answer.
9. What other products do you think have, or should have, regulations about what they can contain?

climate

Is the Earth getting hotter?

You are going to take part in a conference of scientists, past and present, to decide whether the world's climate is changing. Is global warming really happening? And if it is, should we change our lifestyles to halt or reverse the changes?

Begin by dividing into eight groups. There are going to be eight presentations in the next lesson.

You will need to research the evidence for or against global warming. The fact boxes here will get you started. There is extra information for Groups 1 to 7 on the Science Web website at:

http://www.nelsonthornes.com/scienceweb.htm

GROUP 1
Naturalists who study weird effects

Those who watch the behaviour of birds, animals or plants can often see changes due to weather that is hotter or colder than average. These naturalists can tell us about the migration habits of birds, the colour of frogs and tadpoles, and the plants that grew in our country many years ago. Is the Earth really getting warmer?

GROUP 2
Ice Age geologists

We know there have been Ice Ages before, some quite recently, and also warm periods in between them. How do we know this? Are we sure? Are we due for another Ice Age now? And then the really difficult question - why do we have Ice Ages? Is it because the Sun gets cooler, or because the atmosphere gets too murky with dust, or because the rotation of the Earth is different – or something else?

GROUP 3
Where does all the carbon dioxide come from and go to?

For this you have to find out all the natural ways in which carbon dioxide can get into the atmosphere, the natural ways in which carbon dioxide can be absorbed out of the atmosphere, and the artificial ways in which carbon dioxide can be released into the atmosphere. Think about slow processes and fast processes; processes on land, in forests, and in the oceans.

GROUP 4
Are we really increasing the carbon dioxide?

How do scientists measure the amount of carbon dioxide in the atmosphere? A scientist wanted to set up an accurate experiment to measure it carefully. He needed to go somewhere where the world's carbon dioxide is as near as possible to average for the whole atmosphere. Where did he go?

How well do we understand the circulation of air in the atmosphere? What is the Keeling Curve and how does it help us to understand what's happening in the atmosphere?

GROUP 5
Bad weather and the 'Rio Earth Summit'

Weather was bad during the 1980s – droughts in the USA, in parts of Africa and Asia the monsoon failed, forest fires in Australia and some terrible floods in Bangladesh. Thousands of people lost their lives.

The United Nations decided to set up an Intergovernmental Panel on Climate Change (IPCC). By 1989 their first report was ready. It said that scientists were now certain that the climate was definitely getting warmer. The IPCC held its first meeting in Rio de Janeiro, Brazil.

The different countries argued. So the scientists in IPCC were sent off to do some more work. The next IPCC meeting was held in Madrid in 1995. The scientists had done more calculations. They said that 'the evidence suggests that there is discernible human influence on the global climate'. That meant that our man-made carbon dioxide was causing global warming.

There are heated arguments going on about a 'carbon tax'. What is it and how might it affect the rate of climate change?

GROUP 6
Professor Svante Arrhenius and friends

Arrhenius was a Swedish chemist who was born in the mid-nineteenth century. He was the first to realise that carbon dioxide would absorb heat coming from the Sun through to the Earth, rather like the way in which air inside a greenhouse becomes hot. Gradually, other scientists found out about how the different gases in the air behave when they are heated. Some reach a higher temperature than others.

GROUP 7
Will the UK boil or freeze?

Britain may not just warm up like the rest of the world – it might freeze up in a mini-Ice Age, as it did from the 14th century to the 18th century. If you look at our latitude (how far we are from the North Pole), it turns out that we are very much warmer than most other countries on the same latitude. Most of Britain is on latitudes in the 50s. That is the same as Labrador. But a stream of warm water (the Gulf Stream) from the Caribbean flows up to our west coast.

But global warming might change the direction of the Gulf Stream, leaving Britain very cold indeed. When that happened before, the winters were very severe. The river Thames froze, people could roast whole pigs on the ice. Glaciers on the mountains pushed downwards and destroyed whole villages.

Scientists are carefully taking the temperature of the North Atlantic to monitor the 'health' of the Gulf Stream. They are doing the same in the Pacific Ocean, using a computer model to predict the dreaded 'El Niño' flow of warm water.

GROUP 8

This group must find out its own information. The topic for this group is:

'Trees, petrol and green ways of living. What differences can we make?'

This group should plan a questionnaire and use it to find out what people – teachers and pupils in the school, and parents at home – think about climate change. What changes do they think should happen? What lifestyle changes are they prepared to make themselves?

Chemicals can be good for you

All substances are chemicals. Some, such as water and salt, occur naturally. Other chemicals, such as plastics, are artificial. Because a chemical is artificial it doesn't mean it's 'bad'. Equally, a natural chemical is not necessarily 'good'. Kelly, Jo and Chris put this to the test in the supermarket.

You can buy pure water, but it's not nice to drink. It's sold as distilled water to top up car batteries. Water is a very good solvent. Many chemicals dissolve in water. That's one reason why tap water and bottled water contain traces of other chemicals. These chemicals are only present in very, very small amounts.

Sodium fluoride in small quantities can prevent tooth decay. In large quantities it can be toxic – dangerous to some parts of the body. Only very small amounts are in toothpaste. Small amounts are often measured in parts per million (ppm). It is very difficult to imagine these small amounts. To give you some idea – one part per million is one second in 12 days of your life!

We can help prevent tooth decay by using toothpaste containing fluoride. It's up to each of us what toothpaste we use. Some people may not look after their teeth. So some water companies add fluoride to the water supply. All the people using that water supply have the 'benefit' of fluoride – whether they want it or not. About 12 per cent of the British population has fluoride in their water supply.

QUESTIONS

1. What is the difference between 'pure' water and 'natural' water?
2. Suggest how Chris might have got the impression that 'all chemicals are bad'.
3. Why do you think Kelly's dad thinks bottled or tap water is better to drink than pure water?
4. Science tells us what's possible – we can prevent tooth decay by adding fluoride to water. Whether we should do it or not is an ethical decision.
   List the advantages and disadvantages of adding fluoride to water for the following people:
   a) people who use the water supply
   b) dentists
   c) the water company.
5. Chris, Kelly and Jo are talking about whether fluoride should be added to their water supply. Write a conversation between them.
6. Suppose scientists found that adding extra calcium to milk made people's bones stronger. **How** should milk producers decide whether to add extra calcium to all their milk?

Chemicals for food – and bombs!

As the world population keeps growing, more food is needed to feed more and more people. At the beginning of the twentieth century farmers used natural fertilisers such as manure, compost and even bird droppings to help grow healthy and plentiful crops. However, as the demand for food increased the farmers realised they needed vast amounts of fertilisers to grow sufficient food for everyone.

Ammonia – the raw material

Scientists began to research how they could make chemical fertilisers to help feed the growing population. In order to make chemical fertilisers they realised that they needed to make a starting material called ammonia. Ammonia is a compound with the formula NH_3.

In 1900 the traditional method for making ammonia was difficult and expensive. However, by 1908, a brilliant German chemist called Fritz Haber discovered a cheap way to make ammonia. His method involved combining the elements nitrogen and hydrogen directly together in a process that became known as the Haber process. Combining elements together directly to make a compound is known as 'direct synthesis'.

Haber's method for making ammonia was cheap because of where he got his raw materials from. For his supply of nitrogen he took the nitrogen gas out of the air. For his supply of hydrogen he used water or natural gas. All these starting materials were plentiful and cheap. Haber knew that nitrogen and hydrogen would not react if he just mixed them together. He used his understanding of chemistry to work out the necessary conditions that had to be used to make the chemical reaction occur. He realised that high pressure, high temperature and a substance called a catalyst were needed.

Fritz Haber.

As well as being used to make fertilisers, ammonia is also used to make explosives. Explosives have important uses in times of peace such as mining, quarrying and tunnelling, but they are also used in war. This means that as well as the Haber process being responsible for feeding millions of people it also has some responsibility for many, many deaths in the two world wars.

The patriotic chemist

Fritz Haber was born in 1868 in Germany and he studied science in Berlin. By 1912 he was one of the most respected scientists in the country and he was made head of one of the most important scientific centres. One of the first things he was asked to do was to work on a safety device to detect dangerous gases in mines. As war approached Haber, like scientists in France and Britain, was asked to think about how science could be used to help win the war. The German government asked Haber to look into chemical warfare. This meant looking at how chemicals could be used to win the war.

Troops gassed by mustard gas during the First World War.

36   *Haber's apparatus for making ammonia.*

The Russians had already tried using poisonous gases against their enemies, but they had been unsuccessful. In the early months of the First World War they had tried to use chlorine as a poisonous gas against the Germans. But in the cold winter the gas had just sunk into the snow. The following spring, when the weather was warm again, and the enemy was far away, the gas reappeared from the ground!

Haber's 'successes'

Haber's task was to look at how he could release poisonous gases onto the enemy successfully and not poison the German soldiers. In April 1915, the Germans released 5000 cylinders of the poisonous gas, chlorine, against French and Canadian troops. This time it worked

with awful consequences. 15000 troops were injured and one third of these casualties proved fatal. Later in the same battle, the Allies also used poisonous gases against the Germans, which showed that they too had been working on chemical warfare.

Haber continued to work on developing poisonous gases and developed one known as mustard gas. He wanted the German government to use massive gas attacks on all allied troops to end the war quickly. However, the military felt that gas attacks would not work effectively and so little use was made of them during the First World War.

Sadly, Haber's wife was so tormented about the way in which her husband's work had been used to kill others that, in 1916, she committed suicide. Haber himself had no such worries. He declared himself a patriot and said, 'A man belongs to the world in times of peace, but to his country in times of war'.

Haber's rise ... and fall

After Germany lost the First World War the Allies imposed huge fines on Germany to pay for war damage. These were known as the 'Reparations' and the amount needed was equivalent to fifty thousand tons of gold. Haber had heard that the oceans contained millions of tons of gold compounds dissolved in it. Haber thought that if he could work out the science to extract the gold he could raise enough for Germany to pay off her debts. His attempts were unsuccessful, but even so he remained a very respected scientist in his own country.

However, in the 1930s Germany began to prepare for yet another war, but the country no longer wanted Fritz Haber to help her. Germany did not remain loyal to Haber, despite his patriotism. In 1933, Nazism drove Fritz Haber into exile – because he was a Jew.

QUESTIONS

1. Direct synthesis is when elements are combined together to form a compound. Each of the compounds below can be made by direct synthesis.

Water	H_2O
Hydrogen chloride	HCl
Sulphur dioxide	SO_2

   Name the elements that need to be reacted together to make the three compounds.

2. In what ways do you think Haber helped the world? In what ways do you think Haber caused suffering in the world?

3. Imagine you are Haber's wife and you are writing to your sister to explain how you feel about his work.

4. Imagine that you are Fritz Haber in 1934, just after you have been exiled. A German radio station has asked if they can interview you. Here are some of the questions they want to ask you:

   a) How did you feel when you discovered how to make ammonia quickly and cheaply?

   b) How did you feel when your attempts to extract gold from the sea failed?

   c) How concerned were you by the fact that so many people were killed by your work on poisonous gases?

   d) Do you feel that you should have thought more carefully about how your work was going to be used?

   e) What did you mean when you said 'A man belongs to the world in times of peace, but to his country in times of war'?

   f) Do you feel badly treated by the German government now that they have exiled you? Use the information in the passage to imagine what Fritz Haber might say.

5. Should a scientist think of the uses their work might be put to or should they just solve scientific problems?

Under pressure

The particles in a gas are widely spread apart and they have a lot of kinetic (movement) energy – they're moving very fast. Because the particles are widely spaced and they move around a lot it means that a small amount of gas can take up a large volume. But it is possible to fit more of a gas into a container if the particles are squashed together into a smaller space. If they are pushed together without a rise in temperature then the particles will be so close together that they will become a liquid. This is why, when containers with a gas under high pressure inside are shaken, you can hear liquid sloshing about inside them.

What is pressure?

To keep all the particles squashed together and inside the small container it is necessary to push hard, and to keep pushing hard. The particles still have all the energy they had before and so they move around a lot and hit the sides of the container with a lot of force. This hitting of the particles against the wall of the container means that there is a pressure from the container pushing outwards all the time. The gas particles are still trying to spread out even in the small space of the container. The walls of the

container need to be strong to hold the particles (gas) that have been forced together into a liquid. Containers that are capable of doing this are called pressurised containers.

How do aerosol cans work?

Many substances, such as air freshener, hair spray, deodorant and paint are sold in pressurised containers.

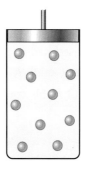

Gas in a large space

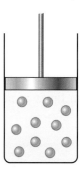

Gas pushed into smaller space

Gas now a liquid because of limited space for particles to spread out and the attraction between the particles

Gas turning into liquid under pressure.

Aerosol cans are used to dispense many everyday products.

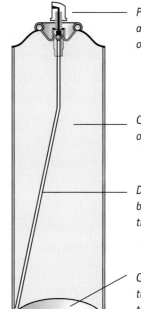

Pressing down on the actuator allows the contents to come out through the valve

Contents are a combination of the product and the propellant

Dip tube reaches down to bottom of container to carry the liquid content to the valve

Curved bottom allows dip tube to reach virtually all of the liquid content

Structure of an aerosol container.

Such pressurised containers are called aerosol cans. Aerosol cans contain the useful material – the product – that is to be sprayed. The can also contains another gas which has also been forced into the can under pressure. It is called the propellant. Both gases are under pressure in the can so both are liquids. When you press the button on top of the can, a valve opens and the pressure is released. Both liquids turn back into gases and the propellant helps push the useful substance out of the can.

Trouble with cans

In the newspaper article shown below, Esther's can of anti-perspirant was left on top of her tape-recorder, which gradually heated up. When the particles of any substance are heated they gain heat energy. This energy is converted into kinetic energy, so that the particles in the pressurised container move about even faster. They strike the wall inside the container more frequently – and harder. Eventually the particles in Esther's can were moving so fast and with such force that the particles burst out of the container. This was the explosion that destroyed Esther's room. As the fireman said, 'Anything that is pressurised and then heated is a potential bomb!'

QUESTIONS

1. Design a poster to tell people the correct way to store pressurised containers. Ensure that you emphasise the dangers of heating pressurised containers.
2. All airlines tell customers not to put pressurised containers in their suitcases. This is because the baggage hold of the aircraft is NOT pressurised. When the plane is at very high altitude the pressure in the hold is very low. Pressurised containers can explode under these conditions.
Use words and diagrams to explain why this might happen.

All pressurised containers carry warnings on the side informing people to keep the container away from direct heat. This can mean radiators, fires, even in direct sunlight on a hot day. Pressurised containers also warn that they should never be burned, even when they are empty. This is because there will still be air inside them. The air will behave in the same way as Esther's anti-perspirant if it is heated up.

£10,000 BILL FOR GIRL'S DEODORANT LEFT ON A HI-FI

Aerosol can blast raises the roof off house

AN aerosol can exploded in a schoolgirl's bedroom with a blast that lifted the roof, blew the door off its hinges and wrecked the walls.

by TODAY REPORTER

Esther Decks 15, was downstairs watching a TV programme about the Apollo 13 mission when her anti-perspirant went off like a rocket.

Her little brother Oliver, five, and her seven-year-old sister Megan were on the stairs at the time but escaped injury. Esther's bedroom menagerie of 43 pets were also unhurt although firemen had to rescue her gerbil from the window ledge.

It would cost £10,000 to repair the damage to the family home in Chippenham, Wilts.

A £1.15 Boots aerosol can overheated on top of Esther's tape recorder.

Warning

Although the machine was switched off an electrical fault is believed to have generated enough warmth to trigger the blast.

Esther's mother Glynis 42, said: "It is absolutely unbelievable that all this damage was caused by a little aerosol can. I know you are not supposed to leave them where they can heat up, but I wouldn't call the top of a hi-fi a hot spot.

"The warnings need to be clearer".

But a fireman said: "Anything that is pressurised and then heated is a potential bomb".

Extract from the Today *newspaper (October 24, 1995).*

Chewing gum – is it good for your teeth?

keep

'Dear friends, we surely all agree
There's almost nothing worse to see
Than some repulsive little bum
Who's always chewing chewing-gum
(It's very near as bad as those
Who sit around and pick their nose)
So please believe us when we say
That chewing gum will never pay;
This sticky habit's bound to send
The chewer to a sticky end.'

Violet Beauregarde couldn't stop chewing gum!

This verse is said by the Oompa-Loompas about Violet Beauregarde, the girl in Roald Dahl's story *Charlie and the*

Chocolate Factory who couldn't stop chewing gum and who, indeed, came to a sticky end!

It indicates that many people believe that chewing gum is an unpleasant habit practised by young people. In fact,

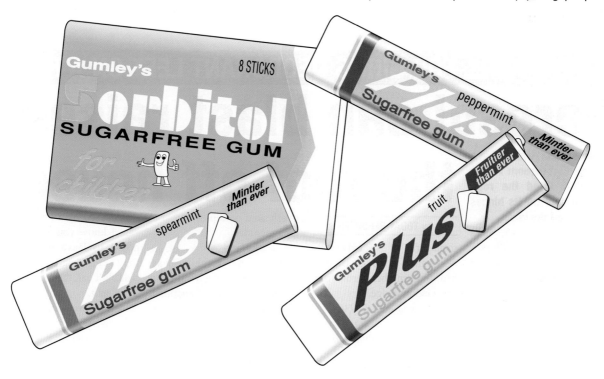

40   *Most modern chewing gum is sugarfree to reduce the opportunity for bacteria to make acids in the mouth.*

nowadays the chewing of gum is often considered to be an anti-social habit. Many schools have rules against chewing gum. In Singapore, chewing gum is against the law and is punishable by fines and even imprisonment!

An old habit

Chewing gum is not a modern habit – people have chewed gum-like substances for many centuries. One of the earliest people to 'chew' were the ancient Greeks. They extracted a resin (a sticky solid) from trees. This resin was called mastic gum. The native American-Indians chewed the resin from spruce trees. People in olden times probably chewed gum in order to freshen their breath because they would not have had toothpaste! But recent research into chewing gum has revealed that chewing sugarfree gum can help in the fight against tooth decay.

The roots of decay

Our teeth are protected by a hard outer coating called enamel. Ninety-five per cent of your tooth enamel is made up of a mineral containing calcium and the other 5 per cent is made up of a protein called collagen, and water. Tooth decay is caused when the tooth enamel is worn away by acid in the mouth. Bacteria, such as *Streptococcus mutans*, are found naturally in the mouth. Acids are formed

STRUCTURE OF A HUMAN TOOTH

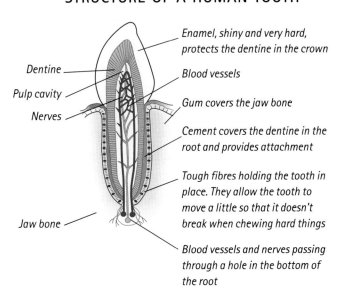

when these bacteria feed on sugar in the mouth. The bacteria, acid and the substances formed by the attacking acids form a material known as plaque. This plaque is very sticky and it sticks to the surface of the tooth. The acids produced by the bacteria eventually wear away the protective coating of enamel and begin to destroy the tooth underneath.

The usual pH of the mouth is about 6.75, but after eating this falls rapidly to pH4.5 (see graph below). This is because the bacteria in the plaque produce high concentrations of acid. These bacteria, trapped in the plaque, can digest any available sugar and continue to produce more acid. This can cause the pH of the mouth to stay low for 20 minutes or more.

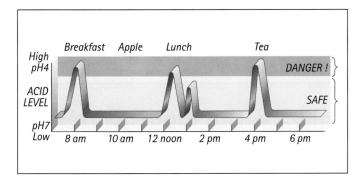

Bacteria commonly found in the mouth produce changes in the pH of the saliva after eating.

Toothpaste secrets

When we brush our teeth we use toothpaste. Toothpaste is a mild alkali. As it is brushed over the teeth it will neutralise the acids produced by the bacteria. This means there is no more acid to attack the tooth enamel. The brushing action also helps to remove the plaque that has stuck to the surface of the tooth. Once the plaque has been removed a lot of bacteria will have gone, as well as any trapped sugar for the bacteria to feed on later. This is why it is important to brush teeth properly so all the plaque is removed. Plaque can also be found trapped between teeth. This can be got rid of by flossing. This is when you pull a long piece of thread between your teeth.

CHEWING GUM INGREDIENTS

Chewing gum base

Synthetic latex gum base: binds together all ingredients and gives a smooth, soft texture.

Sweeteners

Sugar: sweetens and provides a pleasant texture.

Corn syrup: sweetens and keeps the gum fresh and flexible.

Sugar substitutes: eg sorbitol, xylitol, aspartame and mannitol.

Softeners

Vegetable oil products, for example glycerine, help blend ingredients in the gum base and keep the gum soft and flexible by retaining moisture.

Flavourings

Spearmint and peppermint oils: a variety of fruit and spice essences.

Saliva – the mouthwatering solution!

The saliva in the mouth is also an alkali. It too can resist changes in acidity by neutralising the acid produced by the bacteria in the plaque. This means that after about 1–2 hours it can return the pH of the mouth to normal. Saliva is a body secretion that is produced continuously by three pairs of salivary glands in the mouth. As well as being an alkali the saliva also contains antibacterial agents that help to kill the bacteria in the plaque. This stops the production of acid so that the tooth enamel is not eaten away.

Although saliva is produced in the mouth continuously, the flow increases when chewing occurs. Messages are sent to the 'salivary centre' of the brain. Salivary glands then start producing extra saliva. Researchers have shown that chewing gum can increase saliva flow by up to 10 times its normal rate. This is because of the taste and the action of chewing. The extra saliva even becomes more alkaline! This means that the saliva can neutralise even more acid and so prevent even more tooth decay.

QUESTIONS

1. Using the information about the causes of tooth decay, design a leaflet for younger children, aged 7 to 10, to encourage them to care for their teeth.
   The leaflet should include information on:
   • the sort of diet needed to help prevent tooth decay
   • how to care for teeth
   • good habits that will help to ensure that teeth stay healthy.
2. Some people suffer from a condition known as xerostomia or 'dry mouth'. Will they suffer more from tooth decay or less than those without the complaint? Explain.
   What could they do to help their condition?
3. Why is it that many people view chewing gum as an anti-social habit? What could be done to change this view?
4. Examine a chewing gum wrapper. Make a list of the different ingredients and decide if they are the:
   • *chewing gum base*
   • *sweeteners*
   • *softeners*
   • *flavourings.*
5. Scientists who have examined the skulls of people who lived many years ago have discovered that the teeth of these people have nearly no tooth decay. These people did not have toothbrushes and toothpaste! What explanations might there be for this?

Nowadays, even the flavouring chosen for the gum plays a part in preventing tooth decay. Xylitol is the main sweetener in one popular brand of chewing gum while sorbitol is the main sweetener in another. The bacteria in the plaque find it far harder to break down these sweeteners and so the acids that cause tooth decay are formed much more slowly.

Geological changes

Changes in the Earth happen at an incredibly slow rate, so slow, that we can't easily imagine it. Therefore we need to use a 'model' for thinking about it in terms of our experience. In the 21st century scientists now have reasonably good models to explain how and why the Earth changes, but there are still lots of unanswered questions.

Creation stories

Before the 18th century there was no proper science about the age of the Earth, or how the Earth has changed. The Bible had given us the story of Creation, and both Christians and Jews had used that to date the beginning of the world. Bishop Ussher, who was the Protestant primate of Ireland at the time of Oliver Cromwell, did this very carefully. He was an expert in all the languages of the Bible and worked out from all the stories in it the date of Creation. His answer was 23rd October 4004BC at 9.00 a.m.!

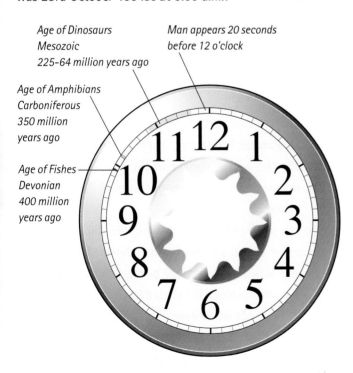

Age of Dinosaurs
Mesozoic
225-64 million years ago

Man appears 20 seconds
before 12 o'clock

Age of Amphibians
Carboniferous
350 million
years ago

Age of Fishes
Devonian
400 million
years ago

Imagine if the whole of the life time of the Earth is compressed into 1 day and it is now midnight.

Bishop Ussher.

WORKING OUT

24 hours = 4 600 million years. 1 hour = 192 million years.

Dinosaurs 225-64 million years = 10.50 pm to 11.40 pm

Man 1 million years = 20 seconds to midnight

Amphibians 350 million years = 10.10 pm

Fishes 400 million = 9.55 pm

Nineteenth-century theories

In the 19th century the debate raged between three theories: Actualism, Catastrophism and Uniformitarianism.

Actualism

This was one of the first theories about how we should think about the age of the Earth. Actualists believed that

changes in the present were enough to explain the slow changes in the Earth. By the eighteenth century fossils of extinct animals had been found, and everyone understood about erosion. Just looking at stones that had been worn round by rushing water was enough to show some change. Volcanoes could erupt and produce new rocks. Scientists have said that 'The present is key to the past', but, like the cooling of a cup of tea, actualists thought that the rate of these changes was probably getting slower and slower. We can't see any changes in the mountains, seas and lakes just because they are so slow, and we only live about 70–100 years.

Lord Kelvin, a famous British physicist of the 19th century, tried to work out the age of the Earth by using the rate of cooling. If you measure the average temperature now, estimate what it was at the beginning when the Earth was molten, then you can find out how long it has been cooling. His answer was that the Earth is between 10 million and 40 million years old. This just about agreed with Indian scholars, who had put the Earth's age at about 5 million years.

But his evidence did not agree with modern measurements. How could rocks be older than the Earth itself? We now believe the Earth is a staggering 4.6 billion years old! What made Kelvin's calculation so wrong was that he left out all the heat energy given out by radioactivity.

Catastrophism

The surface of the Earth gets changed by huge events, such as earthquakes, floods, volcanoes and meteorite impacts.

This theory was first proposed in the 18th century. There had been a number of catastrophic events recorded by myths, fables and written history, including:

● the old stories about the island of Atlantis, in the Mediterranean, which disappeared beneath the sea about 1300BC

● the Roman town of Pompeii, which was destroyed when Mount Vesuvius erupted

● the earthquake in Lisbon that killed 70 000 people in 1755

● huge volcanic eruptions in Iceland in 1783.

All these changes happened quite suddenly. The theory seemed to explain the jagged shapes of mountains and the sudden extinction of animals like the dinosaurs, of which fossils were being found at this time. William Buckland found just the jawbone and tooth of a *Megalosaurus* in 1820. Later, in the 1860s, astonishingly complete fossilised skeletons were found. Mary Anning was particularly good at fossil hunting, finding the first complete *Ichthyosaurus* in 1811. She even managed to support her family by unearthing other fossil dinosaurs in Lyme Regis and selling them to the new Natural History Museum in South Kensington, London.

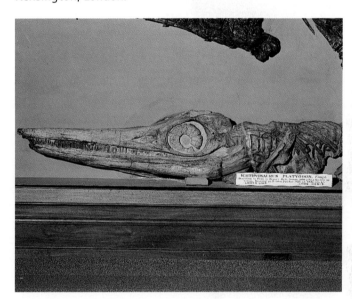

Fossilised Ichthyosaurus *skeleton, found by Mary Anning.*

Uniformitarianism

There are natural influences, such as weathering, that continually change the surface of the Earth in a slow and steady manner. Sometimes, huge external factors cause faster changes.

You can see that this theory, which we still use today, is a mixture of Actualism and Catastrophism. The father of this theory was James Hutton, a Scottish scientist, who lived in the 18th century. He argued against Catastrophism. He wrote 'I can see no vestige of a beginning - no sign of an end'. He spent much of his time in fieldwork, making observations of rock strata (layers) that were laid down, folded, eroded and then laid down again. Strata in the rocks, he wrote, were the 'ruins of an older world'.

Rock strata revealed by folding and uplifting.

Charles Lyell, 19th-century British scientist.

Some of the most interesting discoveries made at this time were by William Smith, a canal engineer. During his surveys for building a coal-carrying canal across Somerset in 1794 he discovered that the strata dipped regularly downward. He wrote that they were like 'slices of bread and butter', and each had its own fossils. He predicted that they would extend right across England. Later he was brilliantly to prove this correct.

But the most famous of the uniformitaria was Charles Lyell. He worked in the 19th century, travelling across Europe and to the United States with his wife, collecting all the information he could. He was particularly interested in the age of mankind and he made extensive notes about the strata that contained prehistoric flint tools. His greatest contribution was to write a huge book in three volumes on *The Elements of Geology*. This took many years of his life!

It sometimes takes one genius to recognise another. Charles Darwin was a great fan of Lyell. When he was setting out on his famous voyage in *HMS Beagle* he took the first volume of Lyell's book with him, and found it very useful for judging the age of the landscape. He had arranged that the second volume would be waiting for him in South America. It was there, but this one was different.

Lyell was arguing that the landscape of the Earth might change but that animals could not. Darwin wasn't so sure and he went on collecting fossils and observing animals.

Years later, when Darwin was going to be presented with a Royal Society medal for his book on the evolution of species of animals, Lyell read it carefully. Then, when people argued against Darwin getting the medal, he announced in public that the book had forced him to change his mind.

QUESTIONS

1. Make a drawing of some strata that have been folded. Show how they might look after a slippage of the rock has made a fault in them.
2. Sometimes it is possible for an older rock to be on top of a younger one. How might this happen? How could you tell that one was older than the other?
3. Write an account of ONE of the catastrophies mentioned on page 44. Choose whether to write it as an eyewitness account or as though you were reporting it in a newspaper.

Houston, we have a problem

The three of us – Jim, Jack and myself – were nearly 56 hours into the Apollo 13 space mission when this famous phrase was spoken. We had taken off from Cape Canaveral on Saturday 11th April 1970 at 1.13 p.m. Eastern Standard Time. We were part of the NASA space exploration programme and we should have been the third crew to land on the moon.

Destination: Moon

We blasted out of orbit and set course for the moon. It's odd really. We were on one of the greatest adventures ever,

The Apollo 13 mission blasts off!

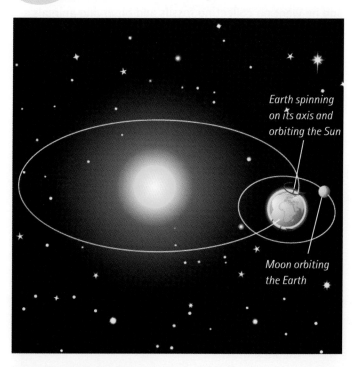

Earth spinning on its axis and orbiting the Sun

Moon orbiting the Earth

Box 1: Earth and Moon
The Moon orbits the Earth every 28 days. It is 400 000 km away.

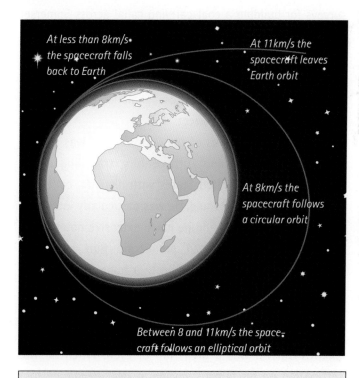

At less than 8km/s the spacecraft falls back to Earth

At 11km/s the spacecraft leaves Earth orbit

At 8km/s the spacecraft follows a circular orbit

Between 8 and 11km/s the spacecraft follows an elliptical orbit

Box 2: Getting into orbit
Rockets take spacecraft up to get them clear of the drag and air resistance of the Earth's atmosphere. Then the rocket accelerates the spacecraft to high speed.

yet everyone sounds so controlled and calm on the radio. Even when the accident happened nobody got excited – we just worked through the problems one by one.

We were just over two-thirds of the way to the Moon when disaster struck. We were performing a series of routine tasks, including stirring the contents of the oxygen tanks that run the fuel cells. Suddenly there was a bang and a huge shudder. The area around our spacecraft filled with flakes of white snowy crystals and we lost most of our electrical power.

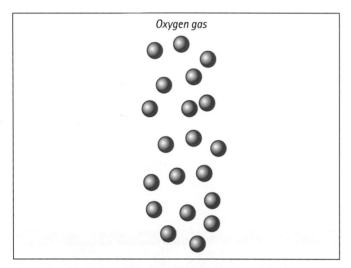

Oxygen gas

Box 3: White snow in space
Oxygen is a gas at the temperatures we live in. In space, the oxygen molecules (pairs of oxygen atoms) lose their heat energy and slow down so much that they form a solid substance.

Power cut in space

We had only a few hours to live at that point, unless the scientists at our Houston, Texas base could find a solution – and they were 250 000 kilometres away. 'Telemetry' is the system that sends data about everything happening in the spacecraft back to base. The scientists studied this information carefully, knowing that if they failed we were in a very expensive, very fast coffin. The effect on our families was dreadful, and all the press coverage and publicity made it even worse.

It turned out that our fuel cell tank had blown up and

we had no electricity to run the spacecraft systems. We could not control the ship. We couldn't make the ship 'roll' to even out the heating effect of the Sun. We were doomed to freeze or boil – and die a lonely death.

LEM lifeboat

Houston came back on the radio. 'Use the Lunar Excursion Module as a lifeboat' was the order. It made sense: it had oxygen, heating and electricity. Sure, it was only designed to last three days, but it was our only hope. We powered up the lunar module and transferred across to it.

A major problem was the electricity supply. With some oxygen tanks gone we had to fly to the Moon and 'slingshot' round it, using the Moon's pull of gravity to turn us around and send us home.

Cutting electricity meant no heating. We huddled at freezing temperatures in our cramped 'lifeboat' as it closed in on the Moon. Our aim was true and we skimmed over the far side – the side that just a few astronauts have ever seen – and rushed away from it on our journey home.

A burn of the rocket motors gave us the correct heading to return to Earth, but something nagged in my mind. Our oxygen supply was fine, but we were breathing out lots of carbon dioxide. Breathable air must have the carbon dioxide removed or you fall unconscious. 'Carbon dioxide narcosis' is what the effect is called. In the LEM the air filters were only intended to last two people for three days maximum. We had three people in there for 4 days.

The Apollo 13 Lunar Excursion Module – the LEM.

Box 4: How fuel cells work
A fuel cell converts chemical energy to electrical energy. The simplest fuel cell uses hydrogen gas, which is made to react with oxygen to form water:

Oxygen + Hydrogen ⟶ Water

Nickel acts as a catalyst and the stream of electrons produced during the reaction creates an electric current that can be used to power components in the spacecraft.

The reaction happens in two parts:
Reaction 1
At the negative electrode, the hydrogen reacts to form H^+ (hydrogen) ions and lose electrons
Reaction 2
At the positive electrode, the oxygen reacts with water and the electrons to form OH^- (hydroxide) ions. The OH^- (hydroxide) ions then react with the H^+ (hydrogen) ions to form water molecules.

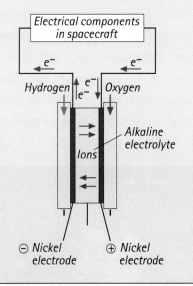

DIY filter

NASA worked on the problem day and night. Eventually they taught us how to build a replacement filter unit using a plastic bag, thick card and sticky tape. We were lucky to find a solution or we would have died in space.

Home at last! The US Navy recovers the Apollo 13 capsule.

Our lifeboat was jettisoned just above the Earth's atmosphere and we came down safely in a flameproof capsule. It was only a week after we had left, but enough adventure for a lifetime!

Box 5: Air supply problem

Carbon dioxide is a weakly acidic gas. You use an alkali such as lithium hydroxide to remove it. Lithium hydroxide is light and convenient. Air is recirculated through the lithium hydroxide granules and comes out fresh – minus the carbon dioxide.

$$2LiOH \quad + \quad CO_2 \longrightarrow \quad Li_2CO_3 \quad + \quad H_2O$$

lithium   carbon   lithium carbonate   water

hydroxide   dioxide

Box 6: How the fault happened

Two faults had happened together:

1. The spacecraft systems had been designed to run from a 23 volt electrical supply. This had later been changed to 69 volts, but one component in the fuel tanks, the thermostat that prevents overheating, was still the 23 volt version. This got too hot and welded shut under the higher voltage, and could not prevent overheating.

2. The oxygen fuel cell tanks had been tested on the launch pad. The ground crew could not drain the oxygen out of them because of a problem with the drainage tube. They used the heaters to 'boil' the oxygen out of the tank. All the wiring overheated, the insulation charred and left bare wire. When the oxygen tank stirrers were switched on, there was a spark from the bare wire which caused an explosion that damaged the spacecraft.

QUESTIONS

1. Give two reasons why a good oxygen supply was important in the spacecraft.

2. Draw a diagram to show how the oxygen molecules might have been arranged in the 'white snowy crystals'.

3. The astronauts moved into the lunar module. What should the module have been used for if the journey had gone as planned?

4. Explain why the build-up of carbon dioxide in the spacecraft was a problem for the astronauts.

5. The lithium hydroxide granules in the canisters react with CO_2 breathed out by the astronauts.
   a) What are the two products of this reaction?
   b) How could you test each product to show what it was?
   c) What other substance could be used to remove carbon dioxide from the expired air?

6. Look at the two reactions going on in the fuel cell. Which reaction shows:
   a) oxidation?
   b) reduction?

7. What advantages does the fuel cell have over other forms of energy supply such as batteries or combustion engines?

8. Imagine you were producing this story as a film. Produce a story-board that would allow you to convey the sequence of events in this hazardous journey.

Cars of yesterday, today and tomorrow

There are about 24 million cars in the UK today. By 2025 this number is likely to have doubled. All sorts of people own cars, but this has not always been the case.

The first cars

Cars of today are very different to the original automobile built at the end of the nineteenth century. The first motor car appeared in 1885. Karl Benz and Gottlieb Daimler designed it. They each designed their own automobile but both used a petrol engine.

When the first cars appeared on our roads they were only for the very rich people who could afford them. This was because nearly all the parts in a car had to be made by specialist craftsmen. There were no car factories then or robots to do the jobs of humans, as there are these days.

The world's first mass-produced car – the Ford Model T.

Mass production

In 1913 Henry Ford began to build cars in large numbers in his car factory. He was the first car manufacturer to use an assembly line. This is where each person in the factory had the same job to do on every car. The car arrived on a conveyor belt and each operator did his or her particular job. The car then moved on to the next factory worker and the next job was done. This proved to be a very quick and cheap way to build cars. Ordinary people could now afford to buy a car. However, they had very little choice as to what they could buy in terms of style and colour. Henry Ford once said to his customers, 'You can have any colour you like as long as it's black!'

Over the years since then cars have changed dramatically. This has been mainly due to customer demand for greater safety, performance, comfort and lower costs.

Where do scientists fit in?

Every car company has a Research and Development (R&D) Department that looks at everything to do with car design. In this department there will be many chemists. Some will look at the different materials that can be used to make cars. Others will look at the chemical reactions that go on when the car burns fuel, whether petrol or diesel.

Karl Benz on the first 4-stroke engine.

Traffic pollution has become a problem in most cities.

One of the main areas that concern all car manufacturers is how to make sure that cars do not produce too much pollution. The UK Government introduced strict laws in the 1990s about how much pollution cars could produce. The laws do not apply to older cars. However, all new cars must meet the minimum pollution standards. The pollution that cars produce is usually called 'car emissions'. The main pollutants produced in car emissions are carbon monoxide and nitrogen monoxide. Both these gases are poisonous gases. They are produced when the carbon and nitrogen atoms in the petrol react

with the oxygen in the air to produce new substances. These reactions are called oxidation reactions. They occur when the petrol vapour is burned, with too little oxygen.

The word equations below show what happens when petrol burns:

petrol + nitrogen + oxygen ⟶ carbon + nitrogen
vapour   monoxide   monoxide

The formula equation for this is:

$$2C + N_2 + 2O_2 \longrightarrow 2CO + 2NO$$

Some particles of carbon are also formed.

However, the pollutants produced can react together and make less harmful gases.

Word equation:

carbon + nitrogen ⟶ carbon + nitrogen
monoxide   monoxide   dioxide

The formula equation for this is:

$$2CO + 2NO \longrightarrow 2CO_2 + N_2$$

This reaction is also a chemical reaction because new substances are formed. It involves oxidation and reduction: the carbon monoxide is oxidised because it reacts with the oxygen from the nitrogen monoxide. This means that the nitrogen loses its oxygen. This is the opposite type of reaction to oxidation, called reduction. The nitrogen monoxide is reduced because it loses its oxygen. However, this reaction is very slow. So slow that most of the pollutants escape into the atmosphere before it has time to take place.

Clean-up time

In the early 1970s one R&D Department discovered that you could use a catalyst to speed up this reaction. A catalyst is a chemical that speeds up a reaction but it does not take part in it. This means it can be used again and again. The chemists discovered that, if they used a catalyst made of platinum, they could reduce the pollutants in the car emissions by 90%. The catalyst can be used over and over again. This means that it can be fitted to the exhaust system of a car and keep on removing the pollutants .

Plastic cars?

Many R&D departments spend a lot of time and money researching how to make cars use less fuel. One way to do this is to make them smaller and lighter. Replacing the steel parts of cars with lightweight metals and plastics can do this. The lightweight metals used are alloys of aluminium, magnesium and titanium. These alloys do not rust like steel does, so it means the car will last longer. Some of the car parts that are starting to be replaced by plastic are the bumpers, the headlamps, water, oil and air hoses in the engine and the body panels and trims.

The safety factor

Safety remains a very important concern of everyone who buys a car. Over the last few years more and more cars have been fitted with air bags and safety glass windscreens. Both of these help reduce casualties in accidents. Air bags are made of nylon fibre. They are inflated on impact. They cushion the driver and front passenger from hitting the steering wheel or dashboard. A tiny microprocessor is attached to an electronic sensor at the front of the car. When the car hits anything at a speed of over 32 kph (20 mph) it sets off a chemical reaction. The chemical reaction explosively produces a mixture of gases that inflate the bag. Cars of the future are likely to have air bags fitted in the seats and the side panels.

Perhaps one of the most striking things about today's cars is the range of different colours available. This has again been due to chemists developing new paints to use on the bodywork. Car manufacturers no longer have to say, 'Any colour as long as it's black'!

QUESTIONS

1. Look at the formula for carbon monoxide, CO, and the formula for carbon dioxide CO_2. Why do you think each is named as it is?

2. There are atoms of carbon, nitrogen, sulphur and hydrogen in petrol.
   a) Write down the word equation to show what happens when hydrogen burns in oxygen.
   b) Write down the word equation to show what happens when sulphur burns in oxygen.
   c) What word is used to describe the above reactions?

3. Catalytic converters have expensive catalysts inside them. Why should this not matter very much to the motorist when s/he buys a car?

4. In 1983 it became law in the UK to wear a seat belt when travelling in the front of a car. Since then the number of injuries and deaths caused by car accidents has fallen.
   a) What sorts of injuries do you think have been reduced as a result of front passengers wearing seat belts?
   b) How will the latest safety features on cars help prevent even more injuries?

5. Design a futuristic car – one that might be around in 2025.
   a) Sketch what it might look like from the outside.
   b) List some new safety features it might have.

Air bags have become an essential car safety feature.

Dyeing for a new look?

Dyeing hair is not a new fashion. 3 000 years ago the Egyptians used to colour their hair. They extracted dyes from plants and animals, including henna (red) and camomile (yellow) from plants. They even used ground-up insects to produce a red dye called cochineal, which we still use today to colour food.

Synthetic dyes for cloth – and hair

In Great Britain in the 1800s chemists became interested in making new dyes. These were called synthetic dyes. They were not used for dyeing hair but for colouring cloth. The textile industry in Great Britain was booming. Cotton was brought from America to the cotton mills in the north of England. This was woven into fine cloth and the new dyes helped create beautiful fabrics to export all over the world.

In the 1920s chemists started to use these synthetic dyes to colour hair. However, it was not until after the Second World War that colouring hair became popular. Nowadays you can experiment with different colours and shades using temporary and semi-permanent dyes. Other people use permanent hair dyes for a complete change of hair colour, or to cover grey hair.

How do hair dyes work?

The different types of hair dyes work in different ways. To understand how each one works it is necessary to understand the way our hair is made up.

There are thousands of hairs all over our head. Each one is embedded separately in the skin of our scalp. The root of the hair is held in place by the hair follicle. A small gland in the hair follicle called the sebaceous gland releases oil onto the hair. This stops the hair from becoming too dry and 'flyaway'. Each strand of hair consists of a central core, called the cortex, and a surrounding thin, scaly sheet called the cuticle.

Hair is made up mainly of very large protein molecules called keratin (see page 54). These molecules are made from many different individual atoms bonding (joining) together. Keratin is very strong and difficult to break. This is why when hair is pulled it does not usually 'snap'; it is pulled out from the roots.

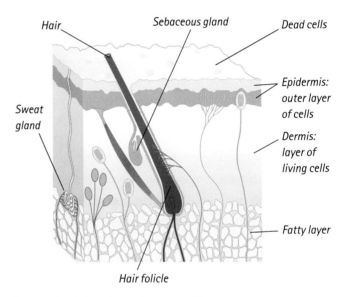

Generalised structure of human skin.

Labels: Hair; Sebaceous gland; Dead cells; Epidermis: outer layer of cells; Sweat gland; Dermis: layer of living cells; Fatty layer; Hair follicle

Temporary dyes
These dyes give the hair a colour that washes out after just one shampooing. They work by coating the outside of the hair strand with a layer of dye. The dye is made up of large molecules. These molecules are too big to pass between the gaps in the cuticle layer of the hair strand and into the central core. This means that they sit on the outside of the strand until they are removed by the next wash.

Semi-permanent dyes
These dyes last six to eight washes. Like the temporary hair dyes, the molecules in the dye are large. They, too, sit on the surface of the hair strand and are removed a little at a time over the next few washes.

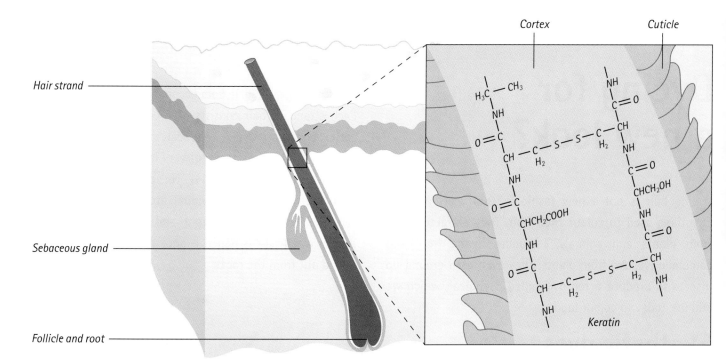

Cortex   Cuticle

Keratin

Human hairs consist of tough, spiral-shaped fibres of a protein called keratin.

Permanent hair dyes

Permanent hair colours last the lifetime of the hair strand. They work by using a combination of small molecules. The first small molecules penetrate the cuticle because they can fit through the gaps. However, these small molecules are non-coloured and would be small enough to be washed out of the hair strand again in the first wash. To make these molecules stay inside the cortex and to make them coloured, another chemical is added. This chemical is usually a compound called hydrogen peroxide. This reacts with the small molecules already in the cortex and makes them join with other small molecules present in the dye mixture. The result is that large, coloured molecules are formed, which are now too large to be washed out of the central strand of the hair. The hair is now permanently coloured.

Hair dye ingredients

The actual number of dye molecules present in a hair dye product is very small. The rest of the preparation includes a number of other chemicals. These include alcohol, ammonia, conditioners and perfumes. The alcohol is needed to wet the hair. This is because water cannot penetrate the oily layer on the hair strand. Ammonia is an alkali.

Reaction 1:

NH_2 $+ H_2O_2$ Hydrogen peroxide $\rightarrow$ NH $+ H_2O + 2\,'H'$

H O

Reaction 2:

NH $+$ H — OH $\rightarrow$ $O = — N — + 2\,'H'$ OH

O OH OH

54 *Chemical reactions involved in dyeing hair permanently. Two colourless molecules combine to form a coloured one.*

It is needed to make sure that the pH balance is right – the chemical reaction will only work at a pH greater than 7. The conditioners and perfumes make the product feel and smell good.

New ideas

Many companies are developing new ranges of colours for hair dyes. These include bright reds, greens and electric blue! However, some companies have responded to public demand for more natural hair dyes. Just as in Egyptian times dyes are again being produced from plant and animal extracts. Hair dyes have now been developed from chlorophyll, the green colour in plants. Spices and cochineal have also been used to produce temporary yellows and pinks.

Nowadays, in the fashion world, 'anything goes'.

QUESTIONS

1. Synthetic dyes are artificial rather than natural dyes. They have been made by the reaction of different chemicals. It is also possible to have synthetic or natural textiles (clothing materials). In the list below there are four natural textiles and four synthetic textiles. List each under the correct heading: cotton, nylon, wool, silk, polyester, rayon, leather, lycra.

2. a) Look at the diagram of the molecule of keratin. Write down the name of each atom contained in the molecule and its symbol. For example:

NAME	SYMBOL
Carbon	C

   b) Look carefully at the two chains of atoms making up the molecule. There are links between certain atoms that make the molecule strong. What is the name of the atoms that are linking the two separate chains together?

3. As hair grows longer, the section of hair furthest away from the roots can become drier than the hair sections nearest the scalp. Why do you think this is?

4. As hair grows, it becomes more damaged. This is caused by constant washing, drying and brushing. The cuticles become loose and, in some cases, fall off.

   a) Whereabouts on the hair strand is this most likely to happen?

   b) Why might this be a problem if you want to put a temporary or semi-permanent colour on your hair?

   c) Use the information above to explain why you should have your hair trimmed regularly.

5. Imagine that you work for a hair product company which has just invented a new hair dye. You are the advertising manager.

   • Design an advertisement for the new hair dye.
   • What might it be called?
   • How might you describe it to encourage people to buy it? Include a little about the science to demonstrate to people how it works.
   • Who might you employ to promote it?
   • You may decide to do a picture advertisement for a magazine or newspaper.
   • You may want to write a short script for a TV/radio advertisement. Remember to include stage directions as well as the dialogue if doing a TV advert.

Weird metal

Mercury is a curious substance. It is the only metal that is a liquid at room temperature, and it is very heavy indeed. Even lead objects float in it. Only gold will sink. If a person tried to float in it, hardly any of his or her body would be below the liquid level. You can see from the picture that it looks more like sitting on a mattress!

The mercury story

The history of mercury goes back a very long way. It was known from prehistoric times that if a special kind of orange stone was heated, mercury could be formed. Imagine the amazement of ancient people when they first saw the silver stream of metal trickling out from their camp fire!

The ancient Egyptians who built the great pyramids were good at making paints and metals of all colours. The Greeks, on the other hand, were not interested in doing any experiments. They thought of themselves as superior thinkers, and left making metals and other experiments to their slaves. But when the Greek Alexander set out to conquer all the countries to the east and south of Greece,

the coming together of Egyptians and Greeks was very good for science.

The great new city of Alexandria was founded in Egypt, in honour of Alexander, in about 320BC. It had a lighthouse that was one of the seven wonders of the ancient world. It also had a library containing more books, probably hand-written scrolls, than there were to be again for more than a thousand years. All sorts of clever people came to Alexandria. There were Greeks, Romans, Indians, Jews and Arabs. And somewhere, possibly a little way out of the city, would have been a community of the people who mined for metal ores, and found out how to grind pure metals with sulphur to make a wonderful range of colours. These were used in making and decorating the jewellery that was sold to kings and nobles. It was very secret work.

Sitting 'in' a bath of mercury.

Droplets of mercury of various sizes .

Maria and the alchemists

These alchemists, as they were called, had to design and build the apparatus needed to purify the sulphur, mercury and other substances they used. They made distilling equipment, the most famous of which is the three-headed condenser made by Maria, sometimes called 'Mary the Jewess'. Hers is almost the only name we still know from that time, nearly two thousand years ago, so she must have been very good. She also designed the 'water bath', which was used for heating plant materials and distilling off oils and perfumes. It was important that these flowers and leaves were not burnt as a result of overheating. (The process works on the same principle as poaching an egg.) To this day the water bath is still used in science laboratories – and in kitchens – and is called a 'bain-marie' in French.

Maria and the alchemists found out that if mercury was heated to a high temperature it would evaporate and then condense into tiny silver drops on the cool parts of the apparatus. These droplets joined together into bigger drops and rolled down into the flasks. Sulphur didn't have to be heated so much, and its vapour was pale brown. But when it cooled down it changed into a pale yellow powder.

Mercury and all its compounds are poisonous – don't touch!

Sometimes it formed circles and patterns on the glass, so they called it 'flowers of sulphur'. It still can be bought today at most chemists.

Strange properties

One weird thing about mercury is that it doesn't wet things – at least, almost never. Mercury forms little drops and even if you poked them with your finger – (DON'T! MERCURY IS A POISON!) – your finger would seem to remain dry. One big drop of mercury can be wobbled until

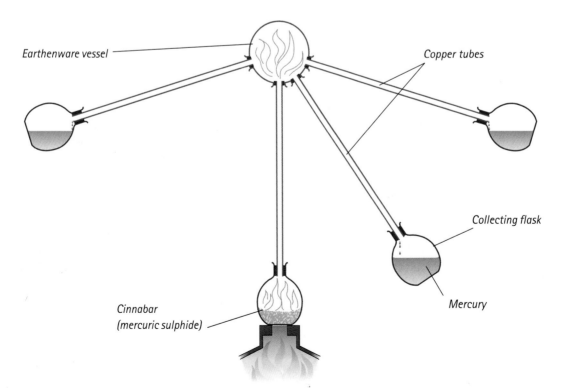

Earthenware vessel

Copper tubes

Collecting flask

Mercury

Cinnabar (mercuric sulphide)

Mary the Jewess designed this distillation apparatus for purifying mercury.

it breaks into two. Two drops of mercury, if pushed gently together, form a big wobbly one.

Why does this happen? It's all because the atoms of mercury are so heavy. That means that they attract each other much more than they are attracted to glass, plastic or anything else. You can see the same effect if you drip water onto plastic (like a sheet of polythene) or onto margarine or butter.

The next weird thing about mercury is that it 'dissolves' in gold. It seems that the spaces in between gold atoms are big enough, just about, for mercury atoms to slip between them. So you might say that mercury is absorbed into gold rather like water is absorbed into blotting paper. There are two results of this. The first is that anyone wearing a gold ring while handling mercury is likely to see their ring turn silver. Well, it is not really silver, just that colour. Thermometers contain mercury, so if one should break in your hand by mistake the little silver drops might well flow past your ring and change its colour. The second result is that gold, which is usually a soft and malleable metal becomes much more brittle. This is because the mercury atoms fill up the spaces between the gold atoms. Then the gold atoms can no longer slip about so easily if you bend the object. Mercury behaves in a similar way with silver and the paste-like mixture of the two, which is called an amalgam, has for many years been used by dentists to fill cavities in teeth.

What's in a name?

Why is mercury called by the name of a planet? There was a time when each of the common metals was named after a planet: Venus for copper, Mars for iron and Jupiter for tin. When mercury had to be named the astronomers may have thought, 'This is a quick flowing liquid. The common people call it quicksilver! So let's call it after the planet that twinkles like silver and moves faster than all the others – Mercury!'

Mercury is the nearest planet to the Sun so it has the greatest pull of gravity on it, and moves fastest. It also keeps closest to the Sun. We can only see it low in the sky just after the Sun sets. In a misty country like ours it is

hard to see at all. If you look near the horizon you may see the planet Mercury shimmering because of all the water dust and vapour in the air over the sea and the land. So it twinkles.

As far as we know there is no mercury on the planet Mercury. It is just too hot. If we want to get mercury on the Earth we have to look for the orange-red ore (stone) called cinnabar. This is a compound of mercury and sulphur. If cinnabar is roasted in air the sulphur turns into sulphur dioxide (a gas that smells like burning sulphur and makes the inside of your nose sore). Liquid mercury will form, unless it is above its melting point of 400°C.

The alchemists' quest for gold

The later alchemists in Alexandria were very keen on turning metals into gold. Finding a way of doing this would be like winning the lottery again and again! They knew that all metals like gold, silver, tin and copper could be mixed together, and they thought that even lead might be turned into gold if the mixture was just right. They did everything they could think of, including singing and praying while they heated the metals, but they made no gold.

Then they found out that if you mixed mercury with sulphur, put it in a sealed flask, and heated it for days and days, it turned an orange-gold colour. This was the nearest that they ever got to gold, and for a long time people thought that mercury (which was cold and liquid) plus sulphur (which was a dry powder and burnt fiercely) did actually make real gold. They said that this was because they were 'opposites'.

Problems with mercury

What do we do with mercury nowadays, apart from putting it in our thermometers? It is used a great deal in industry, especially when making sodium hydroxide and chlorine. The manufacturers have to be very careful not to let even the smallest amounts of mercury escape into lakes or rivers. This would be terrible pollution. First, the shrimps take it in and may die. Then they are eaten by fish, which

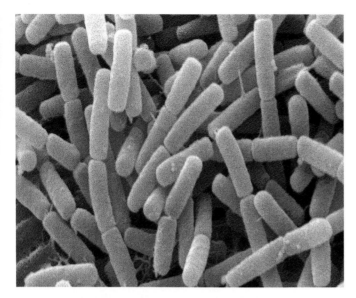

These bacteria eat mercury and make it safe.

might be eaten by people. Mercury is a deadly poison that damages the brain.

Nowadays genetic engineering is giving us a new way to remove mercury from polluted water. In an experiment, bacteria were given genes that let them take in mercury.

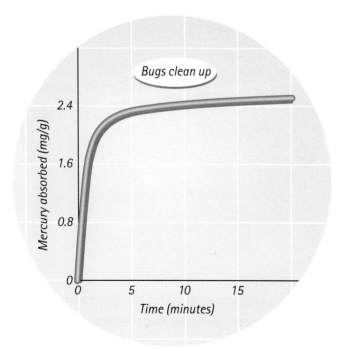

Graph to show how quickly the 'mercury-eating' bacteria can absorb the metal.

Then the scientists added a protein that combined so strongly with mercury that it could not attack the bacteria. So the bacteria can take in large quantities of mercury without being killed by it. Scientists are just beginning to test the bacteria in the polluted water from a lake near New York.

As the graph shows, these bacterial 'mercury munchers' fill up with mercury in a very short time and you don't have to buy any more bacteria when they are used up. You can just let some grow and reproduce in your lake or laboratory. Brilliant science leading to clean water!

QUESTIONS

1. What do you think the orange-coloured substance was that the alchemists made and thought might be gold?
2. Look at the diagram of the early distillation apparatus – the 'Tribikos'.
   a) What form was the mercury in:
      (i) the earthenware vessel?
      (ii) the copper collecting flasks?
   b) What process was going on in the copper tubes?
   c) Why was copper a good material to use in these tubes?
3. Why is mercury good for using inside a thermometer?
4. Why are some dentists becoming increasingly concerned at the use of silver amalgams as fillings for teeth? What new materials could replace this?
5. Look at the graph showing the take-up of mercury by the bacteria. How long does it take for the bacteria to 'fill up' with mercury?
6. Can you find out the name of another metal pollutant in water that is thought to attack the brain and cause Alzheimer's disease?

The beginning of plastics

The story of plastics begins in India and, like most stories of discovery, it also begins with a shortage of materials. By the year 1900 the electrical industry was growing fast in western countries. There still weren't any computers, tape recorders, or television, but there were gramophone records and electric lighting. But there were no plastics for insulation, or for making strong and flexible gramophone records. No one had even imagined them.

Plastic beetles?

At that time, to make gramophone records and electrical insulators, people could only use a substance called shellac. This was made by an Indian beetle that fed on the resin that oozed out of a tree. Many trees can make a resin when they are cut or damaged. The first job of this substance is to heal the wound in the tree by hardening it to keep out bacteria, rather like a plaster on a cut finger. People have found that many of these resins are very useful.

Shellac resin produced by a beetle feeding on certain trees.

All of the following are resins:
- rubber
- **gum for making chewing gum**
- violin rosin
- amber
- **maple syrup**
- **varnish.**

Varnishes had been used for centuries by the Japanese for making their beautiful lacquered boxes, and by artists from many countries for protecting their paintings. Often, the resin has to be dissolved in oil and then filtered to purify it before use. But shellac had already been purified by the Indian beetle!

Shellac was a popular material for producing shiny coatings for precious objects, including Japanese lacquered boxes.

Indians went through the forests looking for shellac and scraping it off the trees, to sell to the industrialised countries. This also removed the beetle and eventually it became very rare. What could be done? Who could make a substitute for shellac?

An artist varnishing a painting.

An early Bakelite radio.

The insulating goo

The odd thing was that many chemists had already made sticky resins in some of their experiments but had thought of them as no more than a nuisance. Who wanted a thick brown gooey substance that could not be scraped out of the flask? The answer was – someone with imagination! If it could be made hard rather than sticky, able to be set into a slightly flexible solid that did not break easily, and be a very good electrical insulator, then it would be just what the new electrical industry needed. Someone might even make a fortune!

Baekeland versus Swinburne

As it turned out, two chemists had exactly the same idea at almost exactly the same time. This sort of thing is called 'multiple invention' and it happens quite often. One of the inventors was a Belgian chemist called Leo Baekeland, who emigrated to the USA, and the other was an Englishman called James Swinburne. It took Baekeland five years of hard work. He decided to make the resin under high pressure – five times the normal atmospheric pressure – in order to make his plastic hard and dense. Then he gradually increased the temperature and his experiment worked! The

Bakelite was an ideal material for mass-produced items, such as telephones.

first ever synthetic plastic was ready. In 1909 he went off to the Patent Office to claim his rights as an inventor. On the very next day Swinburne took his new plastic, made from the same substances in almost exactly the same way, to the London Patent Office. But it was too late! Baekeland had the patent. He called his plastic 'Bakelite', and every manufacturer who wanted to use it had to pay him first, under the patent laws, for the next twenty years. He had hit the jackpot!

Bakelite – the all-purpose material

Baekeland was an inventive man with plenty of ideas. His new plastic was not just used for insulation and gramophone records. Very soon it was made into the handles of kitchen knives and forks as well as for trays, combs, toys, and electric plugs and sockets. But he did not stop there. He mixed Bakelite with sharp pieces of grit to make a grindstone for sharpening knives, and also made ball bearings out of it. These were needed for parts of machinery that had to turn very smoothly. Steel ball bearings were still being used inside the steering shaft of bicycles. Bakelite could be made very smooth and hard. Baekeland showed that, unlike steel ball bearings, plastic ones did not need any grease or oil. He demonstrated in public, for everyone to see, that a shaft with his smooth hard plastic ball bearings could rotate for nine hours non-stop, at nearly two thousand revolutions per minute, without getting hot or damaging the machine. People were impressed. Manufacturers paid to use his new material and – you've guessed it – he became very rich!

Its light weight meant that Bakelite was ideal for portable items, such as cameras.

QUESTIONS

1. When Baekeland made his resin he did so at high pressure and temperature. Why would these conditions have made a reaction more likely?

2. Bakelite was a hard, strong but rather brittle plastic and was used for making many different items. Choose four of the items in the article and decide what they would have been made of before Bakelite was discovered.

3. Today we have many different types of plastic with many different properties.
   Choose four very different objects that can be made from a plastic and describe what properties the plastic should have.
   For example:
   ruler - hard, flexible; electrical plug - hard, good insulator

4. Choose one of the resins from the list given on page 60 and find out more about it.

5. Do you think that patents are fair? Imagine that you are inventing something yourself and you think that someone else is also trying to invent it. How would you feel?

electricity

22 Frogs' legs and batteries

PROFESSOR GALVANI AT WORK...

1 LOOK LUIGI! EVERY TIME THERE IS A SPARK, THE LEG TWITCHES

2 IT MUST BE ELECTRICITY WHICH MAKES THE MUSCLES WORK. I WILL TRY IT IN A THUNDER STORM.

Doctor Luigi Galvani worked at the University of Bologna in Italy. He was interested in nerves and muscles. One day in 1786, when he was examining the muscles in a frog's leg, he happened to touch the leg just as his assistant made a spark with the electric machine in the laboratory.

His wife, who was watching, noticed something. 'Look, Luigi,' she said. 'Every time there is a spark while you are touching the frog's muscles with your scalpel, the whole leg twitches!'

Dr Galvani was very interested in this coincidence and decided to do an experiment. There were no batteries in those days but he thought of another way to get electricity.

He took the frog's leg out into the garden and hung it up, and waited for a thunder storm. He used a brass hook through the spinal column to suspend the legs over some steel wires. When there was a flash of lightning the leg twitched.

3 RIGHT! IT DOES TWITCH

Galvani was very pleased, but then an odd thing happened. He prepared another frog's leg and found that it did not need lightning to twitch. All that it needed, whether it was outside or inside, was to be pushed firmly up against the steel wires. The leg twitched every time!

In 1791 Galvani published a scientific paper to tell other scientists what had happened. He had found that the leg twitched more with wires made from certain metals than with others. He also found that if it was hung up on insulated wires nothing happened at all.

Galvani thought that all people and animals have 'animal electricity', made in their brains, and that this travelled down the nerves and made the muscles twitch.

4 OH DEAR! IT ALSO TWITCHES WITHOUT LIGHTNING

PERHAPS THE LEGS HAVE THEIR OWN ANIMAL ELECTRICITY?

Volta's own explanation was that the electricity came from the contact between two different metals. Volta got a silver spoon and a tin spoon. He then put one on top of his tongue and one underneath it. When he touched the two ends together his tongue tingled.

5 ALESSANDRO VOLTA HEARS ABOUT THE EXPERIMENT...

I THINK THAT THE CONTACT BETWEEN THE METALS MAKES ELECTRICITY

In 1792 Galvani died, but Volta kept up the search. He did a lot of experiments with different metals, using pieces of moist leather or cloth instead of frogs' legs. He built a pile of alternate pieces of zinc and copper. Each pair of metal pieces was separated from the next pair by paper or leather soaked in salt solution.

7

I BET IF I PUT ENOUGH PIECES OF DIFFERENT METALS IN A PILE... WITHOUT A FROG'S LEG IT WILL MAKE ELECTRICITY

VOLTA PUT 50 PIECES EACH OF COPPER AND ZINC IN A PILE

HOORAY! IT WORKS

8

When the pile was 100 pairs high he could even get a small electric spark to jump between the ends of wires connected to the top and bottom of the pile.

Volta was triumphant! Now he was sure that electricity came from the contact between two different metals. He had built the very first electric battery!

Now the two scientists both agreed about what happened but they had quite different explanations for it.

Galvani examined an electric sting ray. He examined the part of the ray that generates the electric shock and reported that this looked very like an animal's nerve.

Galvani thought this was good evidence that nerves make, or carry, electricity. He believed that whenever people are excited it is electricity that makes them feel lively.

6

WELL I DISAGREE WE KNOW THAT ELECTRIC FISH (RAYS) CAN MAKE THEIR OWN ELECTRICITY

QUESTIONS

1. What was it that made Galvani think that lightning would cause the frog's leg to twitch?
2. Why did Galvani eventually change his mind about the cause of the twitching?
3. How did Volta and Galvani's views differ about the cause of the electrical response?
4. What were the three main requirements for Volta's 'battery'?
5. The battery works best when the two metals chosen are furthest apart on the Reactivity Series of elements. Choose the two metals from the Series that would generate the largest voltage.
6. What is the type of energy transfer that occurs in Volta's 'battery'?
7. Find out about the structure of a modern alkaline battery and describe how it differs from Volta's battery.